CKD STAGE 3 AND

DIABETES TYPE 2

COOKBOOK

The Ultimate Guide to Delicious and Healthy Recipes - Friendly Meals With Low-Sodium, Low-Potassium to Maintain Balanced Blood Sugar For a Healthy Living

Lori J. Garcia

Table Of Contents

INTRODUCTION

Understanding CKD Stage 3 and Diabetes Type 2

What is CKD Stage 3?

Chronic Kidney Disease is a condition where your kidneys gradually lose their ability to function over time. There are five stages of CKD, with Stage 1 being the mildest and Stage 5 being the most severe. In Stage 3 CKD, your kidneys are moderately impaired, but they are still able to perform their essential functions to some extent.

In Stage 3 CKD, your kidneys may have a reduced filtration rate, meaning they are less efficient at removing waste and excess fluid from your blood. This can lead to a buildup of waste products and fluids in your body, which can cause various symptoms and complications if left untreated.

Common symptoms of Stage 3 CKD may include fatigue, swelling in the ankles, feet, or hands, changes in urine output or appearance, and high blood pressure. However, it's important to note that many people with CKD may not experience any symptoms in the early stages, which is why regular monitoring and screening are crucial.

Managing Stage 3 CKD typically involves lifestyle modifications, such as following a kidney-friendly diet, maintaining a healthy weight, exercising regularly, and managing other underlying health conditions like diabetes and high blood pressure. Your healthcare provider may also prescribe medications to help control symptoms and slow the progression of kidney damage.

Regular monitoring of kidney function through blood tests and urine tests is essential in Stage 3 CKD to track the progression of the disease and adjust treatment as needed. It's also important to work closely with your healthcare team, including your primary care physician, nephrologist (kidney specialist), and dietitian, to develop a personalized treatment plan that meets your specific needs and helps you maintain the best possible kidney health.

What is Diabetes Type 2?

Type 2 Diabetes is a chronic condition that affects how your body processes blood sugar (glucose). Glucose is an essential source of energy for your cells, but when you have Type 2 Diabetes, your body becomes resistant to the effects of insulin, a hormone that helps regulate blood sugar levels. As a result, glucose builds up in your bloodstream instead of being used by your cells for energy.

There are several factors that can contribute to the development of Type 2 Diabetes, including genetics, lifestyle choices, and underlying health conditions. Risk factors for Type 2 Diabetes include being overweight or obese, having a sedentary lifestyle, having a family history of diabetes, and being over the age of 45.

Common symptoms of Type 2 Diabetes may include increased thirst, frequent urination, unexplained weight loss, fatigue, blurred vision, and slow wound healing. However, many people with Type 2 Diabetes may not experience any symptoms in the early stages, which is why regular screening and monitoring are important.

Managing Type 2 Diabetes typically involves making lifestyle changes to improve blood sugar control. This may include adopting a healthy diet that is low in refined sugars and carbohydrates, engaging in regular physical activity, maintaining a healthy weight, and monitoring blood sugar levels regularly.

In some cases, medications may be prescribed to help lower blood sugar levels and reduce the risk of complications. These medications may include oral medications, injectable medications, or insulin therapy, depending on your individual needs.

It's important to work closely with your healthcare team, including your primary care physician, endocrinologist (diabetes specialist), to develop a personalized treatment plan that addresses your specific needs and helps you manage your diabetes effectively. With proper management and lifestyle modifications, many people with Type 2 Diabetes can lead healthy, active lives and reduce their risk of complications associated with the condition.

The Relationship between CKD Stage 3 and Diabetes Type 2

- *Diabetes as a Cause of CKD:* Type 2 Diabetes is one of the leading causes of CKD. High blood sugar levels can damage the tiny blood vessels in the kidneys, impairing their ability to filter waste products from the blood. Over time, this damage can progress to CKD.

- *CKD as a Complication of Diabetes:* CKD is a common complication of Type 2 Diabetes. Over time, uncontrolled diabetes can lead to kidney damage and CKD. This highlights the importance of managing blood sugar levels effectively to reduce the risk of kidney complications.

- *Shared Risk Factors:* Both CKD and Type 2 Diabetes share common risk factors, such as obesity, high blood pressure, and a sedentary lifestyle. Addressing these risk factors through lifestyle modifications, such as maintaining a healthy weight, exercising regularly, and following a balanced diet, can help reduce the risk of both conditions.

- *Management Strategies:* Managing CKD Stage 3 and Type 2 Diabetes often involves similar strategies, such as controlling blood sugar levels, managing blood pressure, following a kidney-friendly diet, and taking medications as prescribed. It's essential to work closely with your healthcare team to develop a personalized treatment plan that addresses both conditions effectively.

Managing Both Conditions: Importance of Diet

- *Control Carbohydrate Intake:* Carbohydrates directly affect blood sugar levels, so it's essential to monitor your carbohydrate intake carefully, especially if you have diabetes. Choose complex carbohydrates that are high in fiber, such as whole grains, legumes, fruits, and vegetables. These foods are digested more slowly, resulting in a gradual increase in blood sugar levels. Limit simple carbohydrates, such as sugary snacks and refined grains, which can cause spikes in blood sugar levels.

- *Monitor Protein Intake:* Protein is important for maintaining muscle mass and overall health, but excessive protein intake can put strain on the kidneys, especially if you have CKD. Aim for a moderate amount of high-quality protein sources, such as lean meats, poultry, fish, eggs, dairy products, tofu, and legumes. Work with a dietitian to determine the appropriate amount of protein for your individual needs.

- *Limit Sodium Intake:* High sodium intake can lead to high blood pressure and fluid retention, which can exacerbate both CKD and diabetes. Limit your sodium intake by choosing fresh, whole foods and avoiding processed and packaged foods, which are often high in sodium. Use herbs, spices, and other flavorings to season your meals instead of salt.

- *Choose Kidney-Friendly Foods:* Certain foods are particularly beneficial for kidney health. These include foods rich in antioxidants, such as berries, cherries, red bell peppers, and cabbage. Omega-3 fatty acids found in fatty fish like salmon and mackerel can also help reduce inflammation and protect kidney function. Additionally, foods that are low in potassium and phosphorus, such as apples, grapes, cauliflower, and green beans, are suitable choices for individuals with CKD.

- ***Monitor Fluid Intake:*** If you have CKD, your kidneys may have difficulty regulating fluid balance, leading to fluid retention and swelling. Limiting fluid intake may be necessary, especially if you're experiencing symptoms of fluid overload. Be mindful of your fluid intake, including beverages and foods with high water content, and consult with your healthcare provider or dietitian for personalized recommendations.

- ***Practice Portion Control:*** Controlling portion sizes is essential for managing both blood sugar levels and kidney health. Eating smaller, more frequent meals throughout the day can help prevent spikes in blood sugar levels and reduce the burden on your kidneys. Use measuring cups, spoons, and food scales to portion out your meals and snacks accurately.

- ***Stay Hydrated with Healthy Beverages:*** Water is the best beverage choice for staying hydrated, but you may need to limit your fluid intake if you have CKD and are experiencing fluid retention. Opt for unsweetened beverages such as herbal tea, infused water, and sugar-free drinks. Limit or avoid sugary beverages and alcohol, which can contribute to high blood sugar levels and dehydration.

- ***Work with a Dietitian:*** Managing both CKD Stage 3 and Type 2 Diabetes requires a personalized approach to diet and nutrition. A registered dietitian who specializes in kidney health and diabetes management can help you develop a customized meal plan tailored to your individual needs and preferences. They can provide guidance on portion sizes, food choices, and meal timing to help you achieve your health goals.

Day	Breakfast	Lunch	Snack	Dinner
Day 1	Low Glycemic Breakfast Option 1 (Kcal: 350)	Salad with Grilled Chicken Breast (Kcal: 400)	Veggie Sticks with Yogurt Dip (Kcal: 120)	Sugar-Free Baked Salmon with Steamed Vegetables (Kcal: 400)
Day 2	High-Protein Breakfast Option 1 (Kcal: 400)	Lentil Soup with Whole Grain Bread (Kcal: 350)	Sugar-Free Greek Yogurt Parfait (Kcal: 180)	Stir-Fried Tofu with Mixed Vegetables (Kcal: 350)
Day 3	Low Glycemic Breakfast Option 2 (Kcal: 300)	Quinoa Salad with Chickpeas and Feta Cheese (Kcal: 350)	Sugar-Free Chia Seed Pudding (Kcal: 250)	Baked Chicken Breast with Roasted Sweet Potatoes (Kcal: 400)

Day	Breakfast	Lunch	Snack	Dinner
Day 4	High-Protein Breakfast Option 2 (Kcal: 400)	Greek-style Turkey Wrap with Whole Grain Tortilla (Kcal: 350)	Almond and Date Energy Bites (Kcal: 150)	Eggplant and Chickpea Tagine (Kcal: 300)
Day 5	Low Glycemic Breakfast Option 3 (Kcal: 350)	Mediterranean Quinoa Salad (Kcal: 320)	Sugar-Free Berry Yogurt Parfait (Kcal: 180)	Sugar-Free Coconut Mango Popsicles (Kcal: 120)
Day 6	High-Protein Breakfast Option 3 (Kcal: 400)	Lentil and Vegetable Curry (Kcal: 350)	Sugar-Free Peanut Butter Chocolate Chia Pudding (Kcal: 250)	Grilled Salmon with Asparagus and Quinoa (Kcal: 400)

Day	Breakfast	Lunch	Snack	Dinner
Day 7	Low Glycemic Breakfast Option 4 (Kcal: 300)	Roasted Vegetable Quinoa Bowl (Kcal: 380)	Sugar-Free Baked Apples (Kcal: 150)	Tofu and Vegetable Stir-Fry (Kcal: 320)
Day 8	High-Protein Breakfast Option 4 (Kcal: 400)	Greek Yogurt Chicken Salad Wrap (Kcal: 350)	Sugar-Free Coconut Mango Popsicles (Kcal: 120)	Sugar-Free Berry Yogurt Parfait (Kcal: 180)
Day 9	Low Glycemic Breakfast Option 5 (Kcal: 350)	Mediterranean Chickpea Salad (Kcal: 320)	Sugar-Free Baked Pears with Cinnamon (Kcal: 120)	Baked Tilapia with Quinoa Pilaf (Kcal: 380)

Day	Breakfast	Lunch	Snack	Dinner
Day 10	High-Protein Breakfast Option 5 (Kcal: 400)	Turkey and Avocado Wrap with Side Salad (Kcal: 350)	Sugar-Free Almond Butter Chocolate Chia Pudding (Kcal: 250)	Sugar-Free Almond Butter Chocolate Chia Pudding (Kcal: 250)
Day 11	Low Glycemic Breakfast Option 1 (Kcal: 350)	Chicken Caesar Salad with Sugar-Free Dressing (Kcal: 380)	Sugar-Free Chia Seed Pudding (Kcal: 250)	Grilled Shrimp Skewers with Quinoa Salad (Kcal: 400)
Day 12	High-Protein Breakfast Option 1 (Kcal: 400)	Lentil Soup with Whole Grain Bread (Kcal: 350)	Sugar-Free Greek Yogurt Parfait (Kcal: 180)	Baked Chicken Thighs with Roasted Vegetables (Kcal: 400)

Day	Breakfast	Lunch	Snack	Dinner
Day 13	Low Glycemic Breakfast Option 2 (Kcal: 300)	Quinoa Salad with Chickpeas and Feta Cheese (Kcal: 350)	Sugar-Free Almond and Date Energy Bites (Kcal: 150)	Eggplant and Zucchini Lasagna (Kcal: 350)
Day 14	High-Protein Breakfast Option 2 (Kcal: 400)	Greek-style Turkey Wrap with Whole Grain Tortilla (Kcal: 350)	Sugar-Free Berry Yogurt Parfait (Kcal: 180)	Baked Cod with Lemon-Herb Quinoa (Kcal: 380)
Day 15	Low Glycemic Breakfast Option 3 (Kcal: 350)	Mediterranean Quinoa Salad (Kcal: 320)	Sugar-Free Baked Apples (Kcal: 150)	Stir-Fried Tofu with Broccoli and Brown Rice (Kcal: 350)

Day	Breakfast	Lunch	Snack	Dinner
Day 16	High-Protein Breakfast Option 3 (Kcal: 400)	Lentil and Vegetable Curry (Kcal: 350)	Sugar-Free Peanut Butter Chocolate Chia Pudding (Kcal: 250)	Grilled Chicken Breast with Cauliflower Mash (Kcal: 400)
Day 17	Low Glycemic Breakfast Option 4 (Kcal: 300)	Roasted Vegetable Quinoa Bowl (Kcal: 380)	Sugar-Free Coconut Mango Popsicles (Kcal: 120)	Baked Turkey Meatballs with Zucchini Noodles (Kcal: 350)
Day 18	High-Protein Breakfast Option 4 (Kcal: 400)	Greek Yogurt Chicken Salad Wrap (Kcal: 350)	Sugar-Free Baked Pears with Cinnamon (Kcal: 120)	Vegetable Stir-Fry with Shrimp and Brown Rice (Kcal: 380)

Day	Breakfast	Lunch	Snack	Dinner
Day 19	Low Glycemic Breakfast Option 5 (Kcal: 350)	Mediterranean Chickpea Salad (Kcal: 320)	Sugar-Free Almond Butter Chocolate Chia Pudding (Kcal: 250)	Baked Salmon with Spinach Salad (Kcal: 400)
Day 20	High-Protein Breakfast Option 5 (Kcal: 400)	Turkey and Avocado Wrap with Side Salad (Kcal: 350)	Sugar-Free Mixed Berry Yogurt Parfait (Kcal: 180)	Grilled Vegetable Skewers with Quinoa Pilaf (Kcal: 350)
Day 21	Low Glycemic Breakfast Option 1 (Kcal: 350)	Chicken Caesar Salad with Sugar-Free Dressing (Kcal: 380)	Sugar-Free Chia Seed Pudding (Kcal: 250)	Grilled Shrimp Skewers with Quinoa Salad (Kcal: 400)

Day	Breakfast	Lunch	Snack	Dinner
Day 22	High-Protein Breakfast Option 1 (Kcal: 400)	Lentil Soup with Whole Grain Bread (Kcal: 350)	Sugar-Free Greek Yogurt Parfait (Kcal: 180)	Baked Chicken Thighs with Roasted Vegetables (Kcal: 400)
Day 23	Low Glycemic Breakfast Option 2 (Kcal: 300)	Quinoa Salad with Chickpeas and Feta Cheese (Kcal: 350)	Sugar-Free Almond and Date Energy Bites (Kcal: 150)	Eggplant and Zucchini Lasagna (Kcal: 350)
Day 24	High-Protein Breakfast Option 2 (Kcal: 400)	Greek-style Turkey Wrap with Whole Grain Tortilla (Kcal: 350)	Sugar-Free Berry Yogurt Parfait (Kcal: 180)	Baked Cod with Lemon-Herb Quinoa (Kcal: 380)

Day	Breakfast	Lunch	Snack	Dinner
Day 25	Low Glycemic Breakfast Option 3 (Kcal: 350)	Mediterranean Quinoa Salad (Kcal: 320)	Sugar-Free Baked Apples (Kcal: 150)	Stir-Fried Tofu with Broccoli and Brown Rice (Kcal: 350)
Day 26	High-Protein Breakfast Option 3 (Kcal: 400)	Lentil and Vegetable Curry (Kcal: 350)	Sugar-Free Peanut Butter Chocolate Chia Pudding (Kcal: 250)	Grilled Chicken Breast with Cauliflower Mash (Kcal: 400)
Day 27	Low Glycemic Breakfast Option 4 (Kcal: 300)	Roasted Vegetable Quinoa Bowl (Kcal: 380)	Sugar-Free Coconut Mango Popsicles (Kcal: 120)	Baked Turkey Meatballs with Zucchini Noodles (Kcal: 350)

Day	Breakfast	Lunch	Snack	Dinner
Day 28	High-Protein Breakfast Option 4 (Kcal: 400)	Greek Yogurt Chicken Salad Wrap (Kcal: 350)	Sugar-Free Baked Pears with Cinnamon (Kcal: 120)	Vegetable Stir-Fry with Shrimp and Brown Rice (Kcal: 380)
Day 29	Low Glycemic Breakfast Option 5 (Kcal: 350)	Mediterranean Chickpea Salad (Kcal: 320)	Sugar-Free Almond Butter Chocolate Chia Pudding (Kcal: 250)	Baked Salmon with Spinach Salad (Kcal: 400)
Day 30	High-Protein Breakfast Option 5 (Kcal: 400)	Turkey and Avocado Wrap with Side Salad (Kcal: 350)	Sugar-Free Mixed Berry Yogurt Parfait (Kcal: 180)	Grilled Vegetable Skewers with Quinoa Pilaf (Kcal: 350)

Low Glycemic Breakfast Options

Avocado and Egg Breakfast Bowl

Serving for 1   Prep Time: 10 minutes

Calories: 350 kcal   Carbohydrates: 15 grams   Fiber: 8 grams   Protein: 15 grams

Healthy Fat: 25 grams

Ingredients:

- 1 ripe avocado
- 1 large egg
- 1 small tomato, diced
- 1 tablespoon chopped fresh cilantro
- Salt and pepper to taste

Instructions:

1. Cut the avocado in half and remove the pit. Scoop out a bit of flesh from each half to make room for the egg.
2. Heat a non-stick skillet over medium heat and spray with cooking spray.
3. Place the avocado halves face down in the skillet and crack an egg into each half.
4. Cook until the egg whites are set but the yolks are still runny, about 3-4 minutes.
5. Meanwhile, mix the diced tomato and chopped cilantro in a small bowl and season with salt and pepper.
6. Carefully remove the avocado and egg halves from the skillet and place them on a plate.
7. Top each avocado half with the tomato and cilantro mixture.

Greek Yogurt Parfait with Berries

Serving for 1   Prep Time: 5 minutes

Calories: 250 kcal   Carbohydrates: 25 grams   Fiber: 6 grams   Protein: 18 grams

Healthy Fat: 8 grams

Ingredients:

- 1/2 cup plain Greek yogurt
- 1/4 cup mixed berries (such as strawberries, blueberries, and raspberries)
- 2 tablespoons chopped nuts (such as almonds or walnuts)
- 1 teaspoon honey or maple syrup (optional)
- 1/4 teaspoon cinnamon (optional)

Instructions:

1. In a small bowl or glass, layer the Greek yogurt, mixed berries, and chopped nuts.
2. Drizzle with honey or maple syrup if desired, and sprinkle with cinnamon for extra flavor.
3. Serve immediately and enjoy this nutritious and delicious breakfast option!

Spinach and Mushroom Omelette

Serving for 1   Prep Time: 15 minutes

Calories: 300 kcal   Carbohydrates: 10 grams   Fiber: 3 grams   Protein: 20 grams

Healthy Fat: 20 grams

Ingredients:

- 2 large eggs
- 1 cup fresh spinach, chopped
- 1/2 cup sliced mushrooms
- 1/4 cup diced onions
- 1 clove garlic, minced
- 1 tablespoon olive oil
- Salt and pepper to taste

Instructions:

1. Heat olive oil in a non-stick skillet over medium heat.

2. Add onions and garlic, sauté until fragrant, about 2 minutes.

3. Add mushrooms and spinach to the skillet, cook until spinach wilts and mushrooms are tender, about 3-4 minutes.

4. In a bowl, whisk the eggs and season with salt and pepper.

5. Pour the beaten eggs into the skillet, swirling to evenly distribute the vegetables.

6. Cook until the edges start to set, then gently lift the edges with a spatula to let the uncooked eggs flow underneath.

7. Once the omelette is mostly set, fold it in half and cook for another 1-2 minutes until the eggs are cooked through.

Chia Seed Pudding

Serving for 1   Prep Time: 5 minutes (plus chilling time)

Calories: 280 kcal   Carbohydrates: 20 grams   Fiber: 12 grams   Protein: 10 grams

Healthy Fat: 15 grams

Ingredients:

- 2 tablespoons chia seeds
- 1/2 cup unsweetened almond milk (or any milk of choice)
- 1/2 teaspoon vanilla extract
- 1/4 cup fresh berries (such as raspberries, blackberries, or strawberries)
- 1 tablespoon chopped nuts (such as almonds or walnuts)
- 1 teaspoon honey or maple syrup (optional)

Instructions:

1. In a small bowl or jar, mix together chia seeds, almond milk, and vanilla extract. Stir well to combine.

2. Cover and refrigerate for at least 2 hours or overnight, until the mixture thickens and becomes pudding-like.

3. Once the chia pudding is ready, stir it well to break up any clumps.

4. Top with fresh berries, chopped nuts, and a drizzle of honey or maple syrup if desired.

5. Serve chilled and enjoy this nutritious and satisfying breakfast option!

Quinoa Breakfast Bowl

Serving for 1   Prep Time: 15 minutes

Calories: 320 kcal   Carbohydrates: 35 grams   Fiber: 6 grams   Protein: 15 grams

Healthy Fat: 12 grams

Ingredients:

- 1/2 cup cooked quinoa
- 1/4 cup unsweetened almond milk (or any milk of choice)
- 1/2 teaspoon cinnamon
- 1 tablespoon chopped nuts (such as almonds or walnuts)
- 1 tablespoon dried cranberries or raisins
- 1/2 medium apple, diced
- 1 teaspoon honey or maple syrup (optional)

Instructions:

1. In a small saucepan, heat the cooked quinoa with almond milk and cinnamon over medium heat until warm.
2. Transfer the quinoa mixture to a bowl.
3. Top with chopped nuts, dried cranberries or raisins, diced apple, and a drizzle of honey or maple syrup if desired.
4. Stir well and serve warm as a comforting and nutritious breakfast option.

HIGH-PROTEIN BREAKFAST IDEAS

Salmon and Avocado Breakfast Salad

Serving for 1   Prep Time: 15 minutes

Calories: 380 kcal   Carbohydrates: 12 grams   Fiber: 6 grams   Protein: 25 grams

Healthy Fat: 28 grams

Ingredients:

- 4 oz. cooked salmon fillet
- 1/2 avocado, sliced
- 1 cup mixed greens (such as spinach, arugula, and kale)
- 1/4 cup cherry tomatoes, halved
- 1 hard-boiled egg, sliced
- 1 tablespoon extra virgin olive oil
- 1 tablespoon balsamic vinegar
- Salt and pepper to taste

Instructions:

1. In a large salad bowl, toss together the mixed greens and cherry tomatoes.
2. Place the sliced avocado and hard-boiled egg on top of the greens.
3. Flake the cooked salmon fillet and add it to the salad.
4. Drizzle with extra virgin olive oil and balsamic vinegar.
5. Season with salt and pepper to taste.
6. Toss gently to combine all ingredients.
7. Serve immediately and enjoy this protein-rich and satisfying breakfast salad.

Greek Yogurt and Berry Smoothie Bowl

Serving for 1   Prep Time: 5 minutes

Calories: 320 kcal   Carbohydrates: 30 grams   Fiber: 7 grams   Protein: 20 grams

Healthy Fat: 12 grams

Ingredients:

- 1/2 cup plain Greek yogurt
- 1/2 cup mixed berries (such as strawberries, blueberries, and raspberries)
- 1 tablespoon almond butter
- 1 tablespoon chia seeds
- 1/4 cup unsweetened almond milk (or any milk of choice)
- 1 tablespoon unsweetened shredded coconut (optional)
- 1 tablespoon chopped nuts (such as almonds or walnuts)
- 1 teaspoon honey or maple syrup (optional)

Instructions:

1. In a blender, combine the plain Greek yogurt, mixed berries, almond butter, chia seeds, and unsweetened almond milk.

2. Blend until smooth and creamy, adding more almond milk if needed to reach desired consistency.

3. Pour the smoothie into a bowl.

4. Top with unsweetened shredded coconut, chopped nuts, and a drizzle of honey or maple syrup if desired.

5. Serve immediately with a spoon and enjoy this protein-packed and nutrient-rich smoothie bowl.

Tofu Scramble with Spinach and Mushrooms

Serving for 1   Prep Time: 15 minutes   Cook Time: 10 minutes

---

Calories: 300 kcal   Carbohydrates: 10 grams   Fiber: 4 grams   Protein: 20 grams

Healthy Fat: 18 grams

Ingredients:

- 1/2 block firm tofu, drained and crumbled
- 1 cup fresh spinach, chopped
- 1/2 cup sliced mushrooms
- 1/4 cup diced onions
- 1 clove garlic, minced
- 1 tablespoon olive oil
- 1/4 teaspoon turmeric powder (for color)
- Salt and pepper to taste

Instructions:

1. Heat olive oil in a skillet over medium heat.
2. Add onions and garlic, sauté until fragrant, about 2 minutes.
3. Add sliced mushrooms and chopped spinach to the skillet, cook until spinach wilts and mushrooms are tender, about 3-4 minutes.
4. Crumble the firm tofu into the skillet, sprinkle turmeric powder over the tofu for color, and season with salt and pepper to taste.
5. Cook, stirring occasionally, until the tofu is heated through and slightly browned, about 5-6 minutes.
6. Remove from heat and serve hot as a protein-packed breakfast option.

Cottage Cheese and Veggie Omelette

Serving for 1   Prep Time: 10 minutes   Cook Time: 10 minutes

---

Calories: 320 kcal   Carbohydrates: 10 grams   Fiber: 3 grams   Protein: 25 grams

Healthy Fat: 20 grams

Ingredients:

- 2 large eggs
- 1/4 cup low-fat cottage cheese
- 1/4 cup diced bell peppers (any color)
- 1/4 cup diced tomatoes
- 1/4 cup diced onions
- 1 tablespoon chopped fresh parsley
- 1 tablespoon olive oil
- Salt and pepper to taste

Instructions:

1. In a bowl, whisk the eggs until well beaten.

2. Stir in the low-fat cottage cheese, diced bell peppers, diced tomatoes, diced onions, and chopped fresh parsley. Season with salt and pepper to taste.

3. Heat olive oil in a non-stick skillet over medium heat.

4. Pour the egg mixture into the skillet, spreading it evenly.

5. Cook until the edges start to set, then gently lift the edges with a spatula to let the uncooked eggs flow underneath.

6. Once the omelette is mostly set, fold it in half and cook for another 1-2 minutes until the eggs are cooked through.

7. Slide the omelette onto a plate, garnish with additional chopped parsley if desired, and serve hot.

Protein-Packed Breakfast Burrito

Serving for 1   Prep Time: 15 minutes   Cook Time: 10 minutes

---

Calories: 350 kcal   Carbohydrates: 25 grams   Fiber: 6 grams   Protein: 30 grams

Healthy Fat: 18 grams

Ingredients:

- 1 large whole grain or low-carb tortilla
- 2 large eggs, scrambled
- 1/4 cup black beans, drained and rinsed
- 1/4 cup diced bell peppers (any color)
- 1/4 cup diced tomatoes
- 2 tablespoons diced onions
- 1/4 avocado, sliced
- 1 tablespoon salsa
- Salt and pepper to taste

Instructions:

1. Heat the tortilla in a skillet or microwave until warm and pliable.
2. In a separate skillet, scramble the eggs until cooked through.
3. Assemble the burrito by placing the scrambled eggs in the center of the tortilla.
4. Top with black beans, diced bell peppers, diced tomatoes, diced onions, sliced avocado, and salsa.
5. Season with salt and pepper to taste.
6. Fold in the sides of the tortilla and roll it up tightly.
7. Serve immediately and enjoy this hearty and protein-packed breakfast burrito.

LUNCH RECIPES

Grilled Chicken and Vegetable Quinoa Bowl

Serving for 1   Prep Time: 20 minutes   Cook Time: 20 minutes

---

Calories: 400 kcal   Carbohydrates: 35 grams   Fiber: 6 grams   Protein: 30 grams

Healthy Fat: 15 grams

Ingredients:

- 4 oz. boneless, skinless chicken breast
- 1/2 cup cooked quinoa
- 1 cup mixed vegetables (such as bell peppers, zucchini, and broccoli), chopped
- 1 tablespoon olive oil
- 1 tablespoon balsamic vinegar
- 1/2 teaspoon dried herbs (such as thyme, rosemary, or oregano)
- Salt and pepper to taste
- Lemon wedges for serving (optional)

Instructions:

1. Preheat grill or grill pan over medium-high heat.

2. Season the chicken breast with salt, pepper, and dried herbs.

3. Grill the chicken breast for 6-8 minutes on each side, or until cooked through and no longer pink in the center.

4. While the chicken is grilling, cook quinoa according to package instructions.

5. In a separate skillet, heat olive oil over medium heat.

6. Add mixed vegetables to the skillet and sauté until tender-crisp, about 5-6 minutes.

7. Drizzle balsamic vinegar over the cooked vegetables and stir to combine.

8. To assemble the bowl, divide cooked quinoa among serving bowls.

9. Slice the grilled chicken breast and arrange on top of the quinoa.

10. Spoon the sautéed vegetables alongside the chicken.

11. Serve immediately, with lemon wedges on the side for extra flavor if desired.

Turkey and Avocado Wrap

Serving for 1   Prep Time: 10 minutes

Calories: 350 kcal   Carbohydrates: 25 grams   Fiber: 6 grams   Protein: 25 grams

Healthy Fat: 18 grams

Ingredients:

- 1 whole grain or low-carb tortilla
- 3 oz. sliced turkey breast
- 1/4 avocado, mashed
- 1/4 cup mixed greens (such as spinach or lettuce)
- 1/4 cup sliced cucumber
- 1/4 cup sliced bell peppers (any color)
- 1 tablespoon hummus
- 1 teaspoon Dijon mustard
- Salt and pepper to taste

Instructions:

1. Lay the tortilla flat on a clean surface.

2. Spread mashed avocado evenly over the tortilla.

3. Layer sliced turkey breast, mixed greens, sliced cucumber, and sliced bell peppers on top of the avocado.

4. Drizzle hummus and Dijon mustard over the filling.

5. Season with salt and pepper to taste.

6. Fold in the sides of the tortilla and roll it up tightly to form a wrap.

7. Slice in half diagonally, if desired, and serve immediately.

Salmon and Quinoa Salad

Serving for 1   Prep Time: 15 minutes   Cook Time: 20 minutes

---

Calories: 380 kcal   Carbohydrates: 30 grams   Fiber: 6 grams   Protein: 25 grams

Healthy Fat: 18 grams

Ingredients:

- 4 oz. cooked salmon fillet
- 1/2 cup cooked quinoa
- 1 cup mixed greens (such as spinach, arugula, and kale)
- 1/4 cup cherry tomatoes, halved
- 1/4 cup diced cucumber
- 1/4 cup sliced red onion
- 1 tablespoon olive oil
- 1 tablespoon lemon juice
- Salt and pepper to taste

Instructions:

1. In a large salad bowl, combine the mixed greens, cherry tomatoes, diced cucumber, and sliced red onion.
2. Flake the cooked salmon fillet and add it to the salad.
3. Add the cooked quinoa to the salad bowl.
4. In a small bowl, whisk together olive oil, lemon juice, salt, and pepper to make the dressing.
5. Drizzle the dressing over the salad and toss gently to combine all ingredients.
6. Serve immediately and enjoy this flavorful and nutritious salmon and quinoa salad.

Veggie and Chickpea Stir-Fry

Serving for 1   Prep Time: 15 minutes   Cook Time: 15 minutes

---

Calories: 350 kcal   Carbohydrates: 40 grams   Fiber: 10 grams   Protein: 15 grams

Healthy Fat: 12 grams

Ingredients:

- 1/2 cup cooked brown rice
- 1/2 cup cooked chickpeas (or canned, drained and rinsed)
- 1 cup mixed vegetables (such as bell peppers, broccoli, carrots, and snap peas), chopped
- 2 cloves garlic, minced
- 1 tablespoon olive oil
- 2 tablespoons low-sodium soy sauce
- 1 teaspoon sesame oil
- 1/2 teaspoon grated ginger
- Sesame seeds for garnish (optional)
- Sliced green onions for garnish (optional)

Instructions:

1. Heat olive oil in a large skillet or wok over medium-high heat.
2. Add minced garlic and grated ginger to the skillet, and sauté for 1 minute until fragrant.
3. Add the mixed vegetables to the skillet and stir-fry for 5-6 minutes until tender-crisp.
4. Stir in the cooked chickpeas and cooked brown rice, and cook for another 2-3 minutes until heated through.
5. In a small bowl, whisk together low-sodium soy sauce and sesame oil to make the sauce.
6. Pour the sauce over the stir-fry mixture and toss to coat evenly.
7. Cook for an additional 1-2 minutes until everything is well combined and heated through.

8. Remove from heat and transfer the stir-fry to a serving plate.

9. Garnish with sesame seeds and sliced green onions if desired.

10. Serve hot and enjoy this delicious and nutrient-packed veggie and chickpea stir-fry.

Turkey and Vegetable Quinoa Bowl

Serving for 1   Prep Time: 15 minutes   Cook Time: 20 minutes

---

Calories: 380 kcal   Carbohydrates: 30 grams   Fiber: 6 grams   Protein: 25 grams

Healthy Fat: 18 grams

Ingredients:

- 4 oz. cooked turkey breast, sliced
- 1/2 cup cooked quinoa
- 1 cup mixed vegetables (such as bell peppers, zucchini, and carrots), diced
- 1 tablespoon olive oil
- 1 tablespoon balsamic vinegar
- 1/2 teaspoon dried herbs (such as thyme, rosemary, or oregano)
- Salt and pepper to taste

Instructions:

1. In a skillet, heat olive oil over medium heat.

2. Add mixed vegetables to the skillet and sauté until tender-crisp, about 5-6 minutes.

3. Meanwhile, reheat the cooked quinoa if necessary.

4. Season the cooked vegetables with dried herbs, salt, and pepper.

5. In a serving bowl, layer cooked quinoa, sliced turkey breast, and sautéed vegetables.

6. Drizzle with balsamic vinegar.

7. Toss gently to combine all ingredients.

8. Serve immediately and enjoy this protein-rich and flavorful turkey and vegetable quinoa bowl.

Lentil and Spinach Salad with Feta

Serving for 1   Prep Time: 15 minutes   Cook Time: 20 minutes

---

Calories: 350 kcal   Carbohydrates: 30 grams   Fiber: 10 grams   Protein: 15 grams

Healthy Fat: 12 grams

Ingredients:

- 1/2 cup cooked lentils
- 1 cup fresh spinach leaves
- 1/4 cup diced cucumber
- 1/4 cup cherry tomatoes, halved
- 2 tablespoons crumbled feta cheese
- 1 tablespoon olive oil
- 1 tablespoon lemon juice
- 1/2 teaspoon Dijon mustard
- Salt and pepper to taste

Instructions:

1. In a large salad bowl, combine the cooked lentils, fresh spinach leaves, diced cucumber, cherry tomatoes, and crumbled feta cheese.

2. In a small bowl, whisk together olive oil, lemon juice, Dijon mustard, salt, and pepper to make the dressing.

3. Drizzle the dressing over the salad ingredients.

4. Toss gently to combine all ingredients.

5. Serve immediately and enjoy this nutritious and flavorful lentil and spinach salad with feta.

Shrimp and Veggie Stir-Fry

Serving for 1   Prep Time: 15 minutes   Cook Time: 10 minutes

---

Calories: 350 kcal   Carbohydrates: 30 grams   Fiber: 6 grams   Protein: 25 grams
Healthy Fat: 15 grams

Ingredients:

- 4 oz. shrimp, peeled and deveined
- 1 cup mixed vegetables (such as bell peppers, snap peas, carrots, and broccoli), sliced
- 2 cloves garlic, minced
- 1 tablespoon olive oil
- 2 tablespoons low-sodium soy sauce
- 1 teaspoon sesame oil
- 1/2 teaspoon grated ginger
- 1/4 teaspoon red pepper flakes (optional)
- Sesame seeds for garnish (optional)
- Sliced green onions for garnish (optional)

Instructions:

1. Heat olive oil in a large skillet or wok over medium-high heat.
2. Add minced garlic and grated ginger to the skillet, and sauté for 1 minute until fragrant.
3. Add the mixed vegetables to the skillet and stir-fry for 4-5 minutes until tender-crisp.
4. Push the vegetables to one side of the skillet and add the shrimp to the other side.
5. Cook the shrimp for 2-3 minutes on each side until pink and cooked through.
6. In a small bowl, whisk together low-sodium soy sauce and sesame oil.
7. Pour the sauce over the shrimp and vegetables in the skillet.
8. Add red pepper flakes if using, and toss everything together to coat evenly.

9. Cook for an additional 1-2 minutes until heated through.

10. Remove from heat and transfer the stir-fry to a serving plate.

11. Garnish with sesame seeds and sliced green onions if desired.

12. Serve hot and enjoy this delicious and protein-packed shrimp and veggie stir-fry.

Chicken and Black Bean Wrap

Serving for 1   Prep Time: 10 minutes

Calories: 380 kcal   Carbohydrates: 35 grams   Fiber: 8 grams   Protein: 30 grams

Healthy Fat: 15 grams

Ingredients:

- 1 whole grain or low-carb tortilla
- 4 oz. cooked chicken breast, sliced
- 1/4 cup black beans, drained and rinsed
- 1/4 avocado, sliced
- 2 tablespoons salsa
- 2 tablespoons Greek yogurt (or sour cream)
- 1/4 cup shredded lettuce
- Salt and pepper to taste

Instructions:

1. Lay the tortilla flat on a clean surface.

2. Spread Greek yogurt (or sour cream) evenly over the tortilla.

3. Layer sliced chicken breast, black beans, avocado slices, salsa, and shredded lettuce on top of the Greek yogurt.

4. Season with salt and pepper to taste.

5. Fold in the sides of the tortilla and roll it up tightly to form a wrap.

6. Slice in half diagonally, if desired, and serve immediately.

Tofu and Vegetable Stir-Fry

Serving for 1   Prep Time: 15 minutes   Cook Time: 10 minutes

---

Calories: 320 kcal   Carbohydrates: 25 grams   Fiber: 7 grams   Protein: 20 grams

Healthy Fat: 15 grams

Ingredients:

- 4 oz. firm tofu, drained and cubed
- 1 cup mixed vegetables (such as bell peppers, broccoli, carrots, and snap peas), sliced
- 2 cloves garlic, minced
- 1 tablespoon low-sodium soy sauce
- 1 tablespoon hoisin sauce
- 1 tablespoon olive oil
- 1/2 teaspoon grated ginger
- Sesame seeds for garnish (optional)
- Sliced green onions for garnish (optional)

Instructions:

1. Heat olive oil in a large skillet or wok over medium-high heat.
2. Add minced garlic and grated ginger to the skillet, and sauté for 1 minute until fragrant.
3. Add the cubed tofu to the skillet and cook for 3-4 minutes until lightly browned on all sides.
4. Add the mixed vegetables to the skillet and stir-fry for 4-5 minutes until tender-crisp.
5. In a small bowl, whisk together low-sodium soy sauce and hoisin sauce.
6. Pour the sauce over the tofu and vegetables in the skillet.
7. Toss everything together to coat evenly.
8. Cook for an additional 1-2 minutes until heated through.
9. Remove from heat and transfer the stir-fry to a serving plate.

10. Garnish with sesame seeds and sliced green onions if desired.

11. Serve hot and enjoy this flavorful and protein-rich tofu and vegetable stir-fry.

Mediterranean Chickpea Salad

Serving for 1   Prep Time: 15 minutes

Calories: 350 kcal   Carbohydrates: 40 grams   Fiber: 10 grams   Protein: 15 grams

Healthy Fat: 15 grams

Ingredients:

- 1/2 cup cooked chickpeas (or canned, drained and rinsed)
- 1/2 cup diced cucumber
- 1/2 cup cherry tomatoes, halved
- 1/4 cup diced red onion
- 2 tablespoons chopped fresh parsley
- 2 tablespoons crumbled feta cheese
- 1 tablespoon extra virgin olive oil
- 1 tablespoon lemon juice
- 1/2 teaspoon dried oregano
- Salt and pepper to taste

Instructions:

1. In a large salad bowl, combine the cooked chickpeas, diced cucumber, cherry tomatoes, diced red onion, chopped fresh parsley, and crumbled feta cheese.

2. In a small bowl, whisk together extra virgin olive oil, lemon juice, dried oregano, salt, and pepper to make the dressing.

3. Drizzle the dressing over the salad ingredients.

4. Toss gently to combine all ingredients.

5. Serve immediately and enjoy this refreshing and nutritious Mediterranean chickpea salad.

DINNER RECIPES

Baked Lemon Herb Salmon

Serving for 1   Prep Time: 10 minutes   Cook Time: 20 minutes

---

Calories: 400 kcal   Carbohydrates: 10 grams   Fiber: 1 gram   Protein: 30 grams

Healthy Fat: 28 grams

Ingredients:

- 6 oz. salmon fillet
- 1 tablespoon olive oil
- 1 tablespoon fresh lemon juice
- 1 teaspoon lemon zest
- 1 clove garlic, minced
- 1 teaspoon dried herbs (such as dill, thyme, or rosemary)
- Salt and pepper to taste
- Lemon slices for garnish (optional)
- Fresh parsley for garnish (optional)

Instructions:

1. Preheat the oven to 375°F (190°C).
2. In a small bowl, whisk together olive oil, fresh lemon juice, lemon zest, minced garlic, dried herbs, salt, and pepper.
3. Place the salmon fillet on a baking sheet lined with parchment paper.
4. Pour the lemon herb mixture over the salmon, spreading it evenly to coat.
5. Bake in the preheated oven for 15-20 minutes, or until the salmon is cooked through and flakes easily with a fork.
6. Remove from the oven and let it rest for a few minutes.
7. Garnish with lemon slices and fresh parsley if desired.
8. Serve hot and enjoy this delicious and nutritious baked lemon herb salmon.

Grilled Chicken and Vegetable Skewers

Serving for 1   Prep Time: 15 minutes   Cook Time: 15 minutes

---

Calories: 350 kcal   Carbohydrates: 15 grams   Fiber: 5 grams   Protein: 30 grams

Healthy Fat: 15 grams

Ingredients:

- 6 oz. chicken breast, cut into cubes
- 1/2 zucchini, sliced
- 1/2 bell pepper, cut into chunks
- 1/2 red onion, cut into chunks
- 1 tablespoon olive oil
- 1 tablespoon balsamic vinegar
- 1 teaspoon dried Italian herbs (such as basil, oregano, or thyme)
- Salt and pepper to taste
- Lemon wedges for serving (optional)
- Fresh parsley for garnish (optional)

Instructions:

1. If using wooden skewers, soak them in water for at least 30 minutes to prevent burning.

2. In a bowl, combine olive oil, balsamic vinegar, dried Italian herbs, salt, and pepper.

3. Thread the chicken cubes, zucchini slices, bell pepper chunks, and red onion chunks onto the skewers, alternating between ingredients.

4. Brush the skewers with the olive oil and balsamic vinegar mixture, coating them evenly.

5. Preheat a grill or grill pan over medium-high heat.

6. Grill the skewers for 10-15 minutes, turning occasionally, until the chicken is cooked through and the vegetables are tender and lightly charred.

7. Remove from the grill and let them rest for a few minutes.

Turkey and Vegetable Stir-Fry

Serving for 1   Prep Time: 15 minutes   Cook Time: 15 minutes

---

Calories: 380 kcal   Carbohydrates: 20 grams   Fiber: 5 grams   Protein: 25 grams
Healthy Fat: 18 grams

Ingredients:

- 6 oz. lean ground turkey
- 1 cup mixed vegetables (such as bell peppers, snap peas, carrots, and broccoli), sliced
- 2 cloves garlic, minced
- 1 tablespoon low-sodium soy sauce
- 1 tablespoon hoisin sauce
- 1 tablespoon olive oil
- 1/2 teaspoon grated ginger
- Sesame seeds for garnish (optional)
- Sliced green onions for garnish (optional)

Instructions:

1. Heat olive oil in a large skillet or wok over medium-high heat.
2. Add minced garlic and grated ginger to the skillet, and sauté for 1 minute until fragrant.
3. Add the ground turkey to the skillet and cook until browned and cooked through, breaking it up with a spatula as it cooks.
4. Once the turkey is cooked, add the mixed vegetables to the skillet and stir-fry for 4-5 minutes until tender-crisp.
5. In a small bowl, whisk together low-sodium soy sauce and hoisin sauce.
6. Pour the sauce over the turkey and vegetables in the skillet.
7. Toss everything together to coat evenly.
8. Cook for an additional 1-2 minutes until heated through.

9. Remove from heat and transfer the stir-fry to a serving plate.
10. Garnish with sesame seeds and sliced green onions if desired.
11. Serve hot and enjoy this flavorful and protein-rich turkey and vegetable stir-fry.

Baked Chicken Breast with Roasted Vegetables

Serving for 1   Prep Time: 15 minutes   Cook Time: 25 minutes

---

Calories: 350 kcal   Carbohydrates: 15 grams   Fiber: 5 grams   Protein: 30 grams
Healthy Fat: 15 grams

Ingredients:

- 6 oz. chicken breast
- 1 cup mixed vegetables (such as carrots, bell peppers, broccoli, and cherry tomatoes), chopped
- 1 tablespoon olive oil
- 1 teaspoon dried herbs (such as thyme, rosemary, or oregano)
- Salt and pepper to taste
- Lemon wedges for serving (optional)
- Fresh parsley for garnish (optional)

Instructions:

1. Preheat the oven to 400°F (200°C).
2. Place the chicken breast on a baking sheet lined with parchment paper.
3. In a bowl, toss the mixed vegetables with olive oil, dried herbs, salt, and pepper until evenly coated.
4. Arrange the seasoned vegetables around the chicken breast on the baking sheet.
5. Bake in the preheated oven for 20-25 minutes, or until the chicken is cooked through and the vegetables are tender.
6. Remove from the oven and let it rest for a few minutes.
7. Serve hot with lemon wedges and garnish with fresh parsley if desired.

Grilled Lemon Herb Chicken

Serving for 1   Prep Time: 10 minutes   Cook Time: 15 minutes

---

Calories: 350 kcal   Carbohydrates: 5 grams   Fiber: 1 gram   Protein: 30 grams

Healthy Fat: 20 grams

Ingredients:

- 6 oz. chicken breast
- 1 tablespoon olive oil
- 1 tablespoon fresh lemon juice
- 1 teaspoon lemon zest
- 1 clove garlic, minced
- 1 teaspoon dried herbs (such as thyme, rosemary, or oregano)
- Salt and pepper to taste
- Lemon slices for serving (optional)
- Fresh parsley for garnish (optional)

Instructions:

1. In a small bowl, whisk together olive oil, fresh lemon juice, lemon zest, minced garlic, dried herbs, salt, and pepper.

2. Place the chicken breast in a shallow dish and pour the lemon herb mixture over it, turning to coat evenly.

3. Cover and refrigerate for at least 30 minutes to marinate.

4. Preheat the grill to medium-high heat.

5. Remove the chicken breast from the marinade and discard any excess marinade.

6. Grill the chicken breast for 6-8 minutes on each side, or until cooked through and no longer pink in the center.

7. Remove from the grill and let it rest for a few minutes.

8. Serve hot with lemon slices and garnish with fresh parsley if desired.

Baked Tofu with Roasted Vegetables

Serving for 1   Prep Time: 15 minutes   Cook Time: 25 minutes

---

Calories: 320 kcal   Carbohydrates: 20 grams   Fiber: 5 grams   Protein: 15 grams

Healthy Fat: 20 grams

Ingredients:

- 6 oz. extra firm tofu, drained and pressed
- 1 cup mixed vegetables (such as bell peppers, zucchini, and cauliflower), chopped
- 1 tablespoon olive oil
- 1 tablespoon soy sauce (or tamari for gluten-free option)
- 1 teaspoon sriracha sauce (adjust to taste)
- 1 clove garlic, minced

- 1/2 teaspoon ground cumin
- Salt and pepper to taste
- Sesame seeds for garnish (optional)
- Chopped cilantro for garnish (optional)

Instructions:

1. Preheat the oven to 400°F (200°C).
2. Cut the pressed tofu into cubes and place them on a baking sheet lined with parchment paper.
3. In a small bowl, whisk together olive oil, soy sauce, sriracha sauce, minced garlic, ground cumin, salt, and pepper.
4. Pour the marinade over the tofu cubes, tossing to coat evenly.
5. In another bowl, toss the mixed vegetables with a drizzle of olive oil and season with salt and pepper.

6. Arrange the marinated tofu cubes and seasoned vegetables on the baking sheet in a single layer.

7. Bake in the preheated oven for 20-25 minutes, flipping the tofu halfway through, until the tofu is golden and the vegetables are tender.

8. Remove from the oven and let it cool slightly.

9. Garnish with sesame seeds and chopped cilantro if desired.

10. Serve hot and enjoy this spicy baked tofu with roasted vegetables.

Mediterranean Baked Cod

Serving for 1   Prep Time: 10 minutes   Cook Time: 20 minutes

Calories: 300 kcal   Carbohydrates: 10 grams   Fiber: 2 grams   Protein: 25 grams

Healthy Fat: 15 grams

Ingredients:

- 6 oz. cod fillet
- 1 tablespoon olive oil
- 1 tablespoon fresh lemon juice
- 1 clove garlic, minced
- 1 teaspoon dried oregano
- 1/4 teaspoon paprika
- Salt and pepper to taste
- Lemon slices for serving (optional)
- Chopped fresh parsley for garnish (optional)

Instructions:

1. Preheat the oven to 375°F (190°C).

2. Place the cod fillet on a baking sheet lined with parchment paper.

3. In a small bowl, whisk together olive oil, fresh lemon juice, minced garlic, dried oregano, paprika, salt, and pepper.

4. Pour the mixture over the cod fillet, spreading it evenly to coat.

5. Bake in the preheated oven for 15-20 minutes, or until the cod is opaque and flakes easily with a fork.

6. Remove from the oven and let it rest for a few minutes.

7. Serve hot with lemon slices and garnish with chopped fresh parsley if desired.

Quinoa Stuffed Bell Peppers

Serving for 1   Prep Time: 15 minutes   Cook Time: 30 minutes

---

Calories: 350 kcal   Carbohydrates: 40 grams   Fiber: 8 grams   Protein: 12 grams
Healthy Fat: 15 grams

- 1/4 cup diced tomatoes
- 1/4 cup diced red onion
- 1/4 cup corn kernels (fresh, canned, or frozen)
- 1/4 cup shredded cheddar cheese
- 1 tablespoon chopped fresh cilantro
- 1 teaspoon olive oil
- 1/2 teaspoon ground cumin
- Salt and pepper to taste

Ingredients:

- 2 bell peppers (any color), halved and seeds removed
- 1/2 cup cooked quinoa
- 1/4 cup black beans, drained and rinsed

Instructions:

1. Preheat the oven to 375°F (190°C).

2. In a bowl, combine cooked quinoa, black beans, diced tomatoes, diced red

onion, corn kernels, shredded cheddar cheese, chopped fresh cilantro, olive oil, ground cumin, salt, and pepper.

3. Stuff each bell pepper half with the quinoa mixture, pressing down gently to pack it in.

4. Place the stuffed bell peppers on a baking dish.

5. Cover the baking dish with aluminum foil and bake in the preheated oven for 25-30 minutes, or until the bell peppers are tender.

6. Remove the foil and bake for an additional 5 minutes to melt the cheese and lightly brown the tops.

7. Remove from the oven and let them cool slightly before serving.

Garlic Herb Baked Chicken Thighs

Serving for 1   Prep Time: 10 minutes   Cook Time: 30 minutes

---

Calories: 350 kcal   Carbohydrates: 2 grams   Fiber: 0 grams   Protein: 30 grams
Healthy Fat: 25 grams

Ingredients:

- 2 chicken thighs, bone-in and skin-on
- 1 tablespoon olive oil
- 2 cloves garlic, minced
- 1 teaspoon dried Italian herbs (such as basil, oregano, or thyme)
- Salt and pepper to taste
- Lemon wedges for serving (optional)
- Fresh parsley for garnish (optional)

Instructions:

1. Preheat the oven to 400°F (200°C).

2. Place the chicken thighs on a baking sheet lined with parchment paper.

3. In a small bowl, combine olive oil, minced garlic, dried Italian herbs, salt, and pepper.

4. Rub the garlic herb mixture over the chicken thighs, coating them evenly.

5. Bake in the preheated oven for 25-30 minutes, or until the chicken is golden brown and cooked through.

6. Remove from the oven and let the chicken rest for a few minutes.

7. Serve hot with lemon wedges and garnish with fresh parsley if desired.

Zucchini Noodle Stir-Fry with Tofu

Serving for 1   Prep Time: 15 minutes   Cook Time: 15 minutes

---

Calories: 300 kcal   Carbohydrates: 15 grams   Fiber: 5 grams   Protein: 15 grams
Healthy Fat: 20 grams

- 1/2 bell pepper, thinly sliced
- 1/2 cup broccoli florets
- 2 cloves garlic, minced
- 1 tablespoon low-sodium soy sauce
- 1 teaspoon sesame oil
- 1/2 teaspoon grated ginger
- 1/4 teaspoon red pepper flakes (optional)
- Sesame seeds for garnish (optional)
- Sliced green onions for garnish (optional)

Ingredients:

- 6 oz. extra firm tofu, drained and cubed
- 1 medium zucchini, spiralized into noodles

Instructions:

1. Heat sesame oil in a large skillet or wok over medium-high heat.

2. Add minced garlic and grated ginger to the skillet, and sauté for 1 minute until fragrant.

3. Add cubed tofu to the skillet and cook for 3-4 minutes until lightly browned on all sides.

4. Add sliced bell pepper and broccoli florets to the skillet, and stir-fry for 4-5 minutes until tender-crisp.

5. Add spiralized zucchini noodles to the skillet and cook for an additional 2-3 minutes until the noodles are just tender.

6. Drizzle low-sodium soy sauce over the stir-fry mixture and toss to coat evenly.

7. If using, sprinkle red pepper flakes for an extra kick.

8. Cook for another 1-2 minutes until everything is heated through.

9. Remove from heat and transfer the stir-fry to a serving plate.

10. Garnish with sesame seeds and sliced green onions if desired.

11. Serve hot and enjoy this flavorful and low-carb zucchini noodle stir-fry with tofu.

I want to extend my deepest gratitude to you to have taken your time to explore "CKD Stage 3 and Diabetes Type 2 Cookbook." Your interest in this book means the world to me, and I am genuinely honored to have the opportunity to share this resource with you.

As an author, there is nothing more valuable than hearing feedback from readers like yourself. Your honest reviews not only provide invaluable insights into how this book has impacted your life but also help other potential readers make informed decisions about whether this book is the right fit for them.

I kindly request that if you have found value in "CKD Stage 3 and Diabetes Type 2 Cookbook," would you consider leaving a review on Amazon? Your thoughts and opinions matter greatly, and your review could make all the difference in helping others discover the benefits of this book.

Additionally, I invite you to follow me as an author on Amazon to stay updated on future releases, special promotions, and exclusive content. Your support means the world to me, and I am committed to continuing to provide valuable resources to support your journey toward optimal health and well-being.

Once again, thank you from the bottom of my heart for your support and for being a part of this community. Together, let's continue to inspire and empower one another on our paths to wellness.

Use your camera to scan this QR Code or visit amazon.com and search author name "Lori J. Garcia"

MAIN COURSE OPTIONS

Lemon Herb Grilled Salmon

Serving for 1   Prep Time: 10 minutes   Cook Time: 10 minutes

___

Calories: 350 kcal   Carbohydrates: 5 grams   Fiber: 1 gram   Protein: 30 grams

Healthy Fat: 25 grams

Ingredients:

- 6 oz. salmon fillet
- 1 tablespoon olive oil
- 1 tablespoon fresh lemon juice
- 1 teaspoon lemon zest
- 1 clove garlic, minced
- 1 teaspoon dried herbs (such as dill, thyme, or rosemary)
- Salt and pepper to taste
- Lemon slices for serving (optional)
- Fresh parsley for garnish (optional)

Instructions:

1. Preheat the grill to medium-high heat.
2. In a small bowl, whisk together olive oil, fresh lemon juice, lemon zest, minced garlic, dried herbs, salt, and pepper.
3. Place the salmon fillet on a plate and pour the lemon herb mixture over it, spreading it evenly to coat.
4. Let the salmon marinate for 10 minutes.
5. Grill the salmon fillet for 4-5 minutes on each side, or until cooked through and flaky.
6. Remove from the grill and let it rest for a few minutes.
7. Serve hot with lemon slices and garnish with fresh parsley if desired.

Balsamic Glazed Chicken Breast

Serving for 1   Prep Time: 10 minutes   Cook Time: 20 minutes

---

Calories: 320 kcal   Carbohydrates: 10 grams   Fiber: 1 gram   Protein: 30 grams

Healthy Fat: 15 grams

Ingredients:

- 6 oz. chicken breast
- 1 tablespoon olive oil
- 2 tablespoons balsamic vinegar
- 1 tablespoon Dijon mustard
- 1 clove garlic, minced
- 1 teaspoon dried Italian herbs (such as basil, oregano, or thyme)
- Salt and pepper to taste
- Fresh basil leaves for garnish (optional)

Instructions:

1. Preheat the oven to 400°F (200°C).
2. In a small bowl, whisk together olive oil, balsamic vinegar, Dijon mustard, minced garlic, dried Italian herbs, salt, and pepper.
3. Place the chicken breast on a baking dish lined with parchment paper.
4. Pour the balsamic glaze mixture over the chicken breast, spreading it evenly to coat.
5. Bake in the preheated oven for 18-20 minutes, or until the chicken is cooked through and no longer pink in the center.
6. Remove from the oven and let it rest for a few minutes.
7. Serve hot with fresh basil leaves for garnish if desired.

Garlic Herb Roasted Pork Tenderloin

Serving for 1   Prep Time: 10 minutes   Cook Time: 25 minutes

---

Calories: 300 kcal   Carbohydrates: 2 grams   Fiber: 0 grams   Protein: 30 grams

Healthy Fat: 20 grams

Ingredients:

- 6 oz. pork tenderloin
- 1 tablespoon olive oil
- 2 cloves garlic, minced
- 1 teaspoon dried herbs (such as rosemary, thyme, or sage)
- Salt and pepper to taste
- Lemon wedges for serving (optional)
- Fresh parsley for garnish (optional)

Instructions:

1. Preheat the oven to 400°F (200°C).
2. In a small bowl, mix together olive oil, minced garlic, dried herbs, salt, and pepper.
3. Rub the garlic herb mixture over the pork tenderloin, coating it evenly.
4. Place the pork tenderloin on a baking sheet lined with parchment paper.
5. Roast in the preheated oven for 20-25 minutes, or until the internal temperature reaches 145°F (63°C) when measured with a meat thermometer.
6. Remove from the oven and let the pork rest for a few minutes before slicing.
7. Serve hot with lemon wedges and garnish with fresh parsley if desired.

Beef and Vegetable Stir-Fry

Serving for 1   Prep Time: 15 minutes   Cook Time: 10 minutes

---

Calories: 350 kcal   Carbohydrates: 15 grams   Fiber: 3 grams   Protein: 25 grams
Healthy Fat: 20 grams

Ingredients:

- 6 oz. beef sirloin, thinly sliced
- 1 cup mixed vegetables (such as bell peppers, snap peas, carrots, and broccoli), sliced
- 2 cloves garlic, minced
- 1 tablespoon low-sodium soy sauce
- 1 tablespoon hoisin sauce
- 1 tablespoon olive oil
- 1/2 teaspoon grated ginger
- Sesame seeds for garnish (optional)
- Sliced green onions for garnish (optional)

Instructions:

1. Heat olive oil in a large skillet or wok over medium-high heat.
2. Add minced garlic and grated ginger to the skillet, and sauté for 1 minute until fragrant.
3. Add the sliced beef to the skillet and stir-fry for 2-3 minutes until browned.
4. Push the beef to one side of the skillet and add the mixed vegetables to the other side.
5. Stir-fry the vegetables for 4-5 minutes until tender-crisp.
6. In a small bowl, whisk together low-sodium soy sauce and hoisin sauce.
7. Pour the sauce over the beef and vegetables in the skillet.
8. Toss everything together to coat evenly.
9. Cook for an additional 1-2 minutes until heated through.

10. Remove from heat and transfer the stir-fry to a serving plate.

11. Garnish with sesame seeds and sliced green onions if desired.

Herb-Crusted Baked Chicken Thighs

Serving for 1   Prep Time: 10 minutes   Cook Time: 25 minutes

---

Calories: 320 kcal   Carbohydrates: 2 grams   Fiber: 0 grams   Protein: 30 grams

Healthy Fat: 22 grams

Ingredients:

- 2 chicken thighs, bone-in and skin-on
- 1 tablespoon olive oil
- 1 clove garlic, minced
- 1 teaspoon dried herbs (such as thyme, rosemary, or sage)
- Salt and pepper to taste
- Lemon wedges for serving (optional)
- Fresh parsley for garnish (optional)

Instructions:

1. Preheat the oven to 400°F (200°C).

2. In a small bowl, mix together olive oil, minced garlic, dried herbs, salt, and pepper.

3. Rub the herb mixture over the chicken thighs, coating them evenly.

4. Place the chicken thighs on a baking sheet lined with parchment paper.

5. Bake in the preheated oven for 20-25 minutes, or until the chicken is cooked through and the skin is crispy.

6. Remove from the oven and let the chicken rest for a few minutes.

7. Serve hot with lemon wedges and garnish with fresh parsley if desired.

Grilled Vegetable and Tofu Skewers

Serving for 1   Prep Time: 15 minutes   Cook Time: 10 minutes

---

Calories: 280 kcal   Carbohydrates: 15 grams   Fiber: 5 grams   Protein: 20 grams
Healthy Fat: 15 grams

Ingredients:

- 6 oz. extra firm tofu, drained and cubed
- 1 cup mixed vegetables (such as cherry tomatoes, bell peppers, zucchini, and mushrooms), cut into chunks
- 1 tablespoon olive oil
- 1 tablespoon balsamic vinegar
- 1 clove garlic, minced
- 1/2 teaspoon dried Italian herbs (such as basil, oregano, or thyme)
- Salt and pepper to taste
- Lemon wedges for serving (optional)
- Fresh basil leaves for garnish (optional)

Instructions:

1. If using wooden skewers, soak them in water for at least 30 minutes to prevent burning.
2. In a bowl, combine olive oil, balsamic vinegar, minced garlic, dried Italian herbs, salt, and pepper.
3. Thread the tofu cubes and mixed vegetables onto the skewers, alternating between ingredients.
4. Brush the olive oil and balsamic vinegar mixture over the skewers, coating them evenly.
5. Preheat the grill or grill pan over medium-high heat.
6. Grill the skewers for 4-5 minutes on each side, or until the vegetables are tender and the tofu is lightly browned.
7. Remove from the grill and let them cool slightly..

Garlic Shrimp with Quinoa

Serving for 1   Prep Time: 10 minutes   Cook Time: 15 minutes

---

Calories: 350 kcal   Carbohydrates: 30 grams   Fiber: 4 grams   Protein: 25 grams

Healthy Fat: 15 grams

Ingredients:

- 6 oz. shrimp, peeled and deveined
- 1/2 cup quinoa, rinsed
- 1 cup low-sodium chicken or vegetable broth
- 2 cloves garlic, minced
- 1 tablespoon olive oil
- 1 tablespoon lemon juice
- 1 teaspoon lemon zest
- Salt and pepper to taste
- Fresh parsley for garnish (optional)

Instructions:

1. In a medium saucepan, bring the chicken or vegetable broth to a boil.
2. Add quinoa to the boiling broth, reduce heat to low, cover, and simmer for 15 minutes or until quinoa is cooked and liquid is absorbed.
3. While quinoa is cooking, heat olive oil in a skillet over medium heat.
4. Add minced garlic to the skillet and sauté for 1-2 minutes until fragrant.
5. Add shrimp to the skillet and cook for 2-3 minutes on each side until pink and cooked through.
6. Season shrimp with lemon juice, lemon zest, salt, and pepper.
7. Fluff cooked quinoa with a fork and divide it onto a plate.
8. Arrange cooked garlic shrimp on top of the quinoa.
9. Garnish with fresh parsley if desired.

Baked Eggplant Parmesan

Serving for 1   Prep Time: 20 minutes   Cook Time: 30 minutes

---

Calories: 380 kcal   Carbohydrates: 25 grams   Fiber: 7 grams   Protein: 15 grams

Healthy Fat: 20 grams

Ingredients:

- 1 small eggplant, sliced into 1/2-inch rounds
- 1/2 cup marinara sauce (low-sodium)
- 1/4 cup grated Parmesan cheese
- 1/4 cup shredded mozzarella cheese
- 1/4 cup whole wheat breadcrumbs
- 1 tablespoon olive oil
- 1 teaspoon dried Italian herbs (such as basil, oregano, or thyme)
- Salt and pepper to taste
- Fresh basil leaves for garnish (optional)

Instructions:

1. Preheat the oven to 400°F (200°C).
2. Place eggplant slices on a baking sheet lined with parchment paper.
3. Drizzle olive oil over the eggplant slices and season with dried Italian herbs, salt, and pepper.
4. Bake in the preheated oven for 15 minutes, flipping halfway through, until eggplant is tender.
5. Remove from the oven and reduce oven temperature to 350°F (175°C).
6. Spread marinara sauce over each eggplant slice.
7. Sprinkle grated Parmesan cheese, shredded mozzarella cheese, and whole wheat breadcrumbs over the marinara sauce.
8. Return to the oven and bake for an additional 10-15 minutes, or until the cheese is melted and bubbly.

9. Remove from the oven and let it cool slightly.

10. Garnish with fresh basil leaves if desired.

11. Serve hot and enjoy this delicious baked eggplant Parmesan.

Lemon Garlic Herb Grilled Chicken Breast

Serving for 1   Prep Time: 10 minutes   Cook Time: 15 minutes

Calories: 320 kcal   Carbohydrates: 2 grams   Fiber: 0 grams   Protein: 30 grams

Healthy Fat: 20 grams

Ingredients:

- 6 oz. chicken breast
- 1 tablespoon olive oil
- 1 tablespoon fresh lemon juice
- 1 clove garlic, minced
- 1 teaspoon lemon zest
- 1 teaspoon dried herbs (such as rosemary, thyme, or oregano)
- Salt and pepper to taste
- Lemon slices for serving (optional)
- Fresh parsley for garnish (optional)

Instructions:

1. In a small bowl, whisk together olive oil, fresh lemon juice, minced garlic, lemon zest, dried herbs, salt, and pepper.

2. Place the chicken breast in a shallow dish and pour the lemon herb mixture over it, turning to coat evenly.

3. Let the chicken marinate for at least 30 minutes in the refrigerator.

4. Preheat the grill to medium-high heat.

5. Remove the chicken breast from the marinade and discard any excess marinade.

6. Grill the chicken breast for 6-7 minutes on each side, or until cooked through and no longer pink in the center.

7. Remove from the grill and let it rest for a few minutes.

Turkey and Quinoa Stuffed Bell Peppers

Serving for 1   Prep Time: 15 minutes   Cook Time: 35 minutes

---

Calories: 350 kcal   Carbohydrates: 30 grams   Fiber: 6 grams   Protein: 25 grams

Healthy Fat: 15 grams

Ingredients:

- 1 bell pepper (any color), halved and seeds removed
- 1/2 cup cooked quinoa
- 4 oz. lean ground turkey
- 1/4 cup diced tomatoes
- 1/4 cup diced onion
- 1/4 cup black beans, drained and rinsed
- 1/4 teaspoon ground cumin
- 1/4 teaspoon chili powder
- Salt and pepper to taste
- 1 tablespoon shredded cheddar cheese
- Fresh cilantro for garnish (optional)

Instructions:

1. Preheat the oven to 375°F (190°C).
2. In a skillet over medium heat, cook ground turkey until browned and cooked through, breaking it apart with a spoon.
3. Add diced onion to the skillet and cook until softened.
4. Stir in diced tomatoes, black beans, cooked quinoa, ground cumin, chili powder, salt, and pepper. Cook for another 2-3 minutes.
5. Stuff each bell pepper half with the turkey-quinoa mixture.
6. Place the stuffed bell peppers in a baking dish.
7. Top each stuffed pepper with shredded cheddar cheese.
8. Cover the baking dish with aluminum foil and bake in the preheated oven for 25-30 minutes.

9. Remove the foil and bake for an additional 5 minutes, or until the cheese is melted and bubbly.

10. Garnish with fresh cilantro if desired.

11. Serve hot and enjoy these flavorful turkey and quinoa stuffed bell peppers.

STEW AND SOUPS RECIPES

Lentil and Vegetable Soup

Serving for 1   Prep Time: 15 minutes   Cook Time: 30 minutes

---

Calories: 300 kcal   Carbohydrates: 45 grams   Fiber: 12 grams   Protein: 15 grams

Healthy Fat: 8 grams

- 1 clove garlic, minced
- 1/2 teaspoon dried thyme
- Salt and pepper to taste
- 1 tablespoon olive oil
- Fresh parsley for garnish (optional)

Instructions:

1. In a medium pot, heat olive oil over medium heat.
2. Add minced garlic, chopped onion, chopped carrots, and chopped celery to the pot. Cook for 5 minutes until vegetables are softened.
3. Stir in dried thyme, salt, and pepper.
4. Add rinsed lentils, diced tomatoes, vegetable broth, and water to the pot. Bring to a boil.

Ingredients:

- 1/4 cup dry green lentils, rinsed and drained
- 1 cup low-sodium vegetable broth
- 1/2 cup water
- 1/2 cup diced tomatoes
- 1/4 cup chopped carrots
- 1/4 cup chopped celery
- 1/4 cup chopped onion

5. Reduce heat to low, cover, and simmer for 20-25 minutes until lentils are tender.

6. Taste and adjust seasoning if necessary.

7. Ladle the soup into a bowl and garnish with fresh parsley if desired.

8. Serve hot and enjoy this hearty lentil and vegetable soup.

Chicken and Vegetable Stew

Serving for 1   Prep Time: 20 minutes   Cook Time: 40 minutes

Calories: 350 kcal   Carbohydrates: 20 grams   Fiber: 5 grams   Protein: 30 grams
Healthy Fat: 12 grams

Ingredients:

- 6 oz. chicken breast, cut into bite-sized pieces
- 1 cup low-sodium chicken broth
- 1/2 cup water
- 1/2 cup chopped tomatoes
- 1/4 cup chopped carrots
- 1/4 cup chopped celery
- 1/4 cup chopped onion
- 1 clove garlic, minced
- 1/2 teaspoon dried thyme
- Salt and pepper to taste
- 1 tablespoon olive oil
- Fresh parsley for garnish (optional)

Instructions:

1. In a large pot, heat olive oil over medium heat.

2. Add minced garlic, chopped onion, chopped carrots, and chopped celery to the pot. Cook for 5 minutes until vegetables are softened.

3. Stir in dried thyme, salt, and pepper.

4. Add chicken breast pieces to the pot and cook until browned on all sides.

5. Pour in low-sodium chicken broth and water. Bring to a boil.

6. Reduce heat to low, cover, and simmer for 30 minutes until chicken is cooked through and vegetables are tender.

7. Taste and adjust seasoning if necessary.

8. Ladle the stew into a bowl and garnish with fresh parsley if desired.

9. Serve hot and enjoy this comforting chicken and vegetable stew.

Minestrone Soup

Serving for 1   Prep Time: 15 minutes   Cook Time: 30 minutes

Calories: 320 kcal   Carbohydrates: 55 grams   Fiber: 12 grams   Protein: 10 grams
Healthy Fat: 5 grams

Ingredients:

- 2 cups low-sodium vegetable broth
- 1/2 cup diced tomatoes
- 1/4 cup diced carrots
- 1/4 cup diced celery
- 1/4 cup diced onion
- 1/2 cup cooked small pasta (such as macaroni or penne)
- 1/4 cup canned kidney beans, drained and rinsed
- 1/4 cup chopped spinach or kale
- 1 clove garlic, minced
- 1/2 teaspoon dried Italian herbs (such as basil, oregano, or thyme)
- Salt and pepper to taste
- 1 tablespoon olive oil
- Grated Parmesan cheese for garnish (optional)

Instructions:

1. In a large pot, heat olive oil over medium heat.

2. Add diced carrots, diced celery, diced onion, and minced garlic to the pot. Cook for 5-7 minutes, until vegetables are softened.

3. Pour in the vegetable broth and diced tomatoes.

4. Stir in cooked pasta, kidney beans, chopped spinach or kale, dried Italian herbs, salt, and pepper.

5. Bring the soup to a boil, then reduce the heat to low and let it simmer for 20-25 minutes, stirring occasionally.

6. Taste and adjust seasoning if needed.

7. Serve hot, garnished with grated Parmesan cheese if desired.

Beef and Barley Stew

Serving for 1   Prep Time: 20 minutes   Cook Time: 1 hour

Calories: 380 kcal   Carbohydrates: 40 grams   Fiber: 8 grams   Protein: 25 grams

Healthy Fat: 15 grams

Ingredients:

- 4 oz. lean beef stew meat, diced
- 2 cups low-sodium beef broth
- 1/4 cup diced carrots
- 1/4 cup diced celery
- 1/4 cup diced onion
- 1/4 cup pearl barley, rinsed
- 1/2 cup diced tomatoes
- 1 clove garlic, minced
- 1/2 teaspoon dried thyme
- Salt and pepper to taste
- 1 tablespoon olive oil

Instructions:

1. In a large pot, heat olive oil over medium heat.
2. Add diced beef stew meat to the pot and cook until browned on all sides.
3. Add diced carrots, diced celery, diced onion, and minced garlic to the pot. Cook for 5-7 minutes, until vegetables are softened.
4. Pour in the beef broth and diced tomatoes.
5. Stir in pearl barley, dried thyme, salt, and pepper.
6. Bring the stew to a boil, then reduce the heat to low and let it simmer for 45-60 minutes, or until the beef is tender and the barley is cooked through, stirring occasionally.
7. Taste and adjust seasoning if needed.
8. Serve hot and enjoy this hearty beef and barley stew.

Spinach and White Bean Soup

Serving for 1   Prep Time: 10 minutes   Cook Time: 25 minutes

---

Calories: 280 kcal   Carbohydrates: 40 grams   Fiber: 10 grams   Protein: 15 grams

Healthy Fat: 5 grams

Ingredients:

- 2 cups low-sodium vegetable broth
- 1/2 cup canned white beans, drained and rinsed
- 1 cup chopped spinach
- 1/4 cup diced onion
- 1 clove garlic, minced

- 1/2 teaspoon dried Italian herbs (such as basil, oregano, or thyme)
- Salt and pepper to taste
- 1 tablespoon olive oil
- Grated Parmesan cheese for garnish (optional)

Instructions:

1. In a large pot, heat olive oil over medium heat.
2. Add diced onion and minced garlic to the pot. Cook for 2-3 minutes until softened and fragrant.
3. Pour in the vegetable broth and bring it to a simmer.
4. Add canned white beans and dried Italian herbs to the pot. Cook for 10-15 minutes to allow flavors to meld.
5. Stir in chopped spinach and cook for an additional 5 minutes until spinach is wilted.
6. Season with salt and pepper to taste.
7. Serve hot, garnished with grated Parmesan cheese if desired.

Moroccan Chickpea Stew

Serving for 1   Prep Time: 15 minutes   Cook Time: 35 minutes

Calories: 320 kcal   Carbohydrates: 50 grams   Fiber: 15 grams   Protein: 12 grams
Healthy Fat: 10 grams

Ingredients:

- 2 cups low-sodium vegetable broth
- 1/2 cup canned chickpeas, drained and rinsed
- 1/4 cup diced tomatoes
- 1/4 cup diced carrots
- 1/4 cup diced zucchini
- 1/4 cup diced onion

- 1 clove garlic, minced
- 1/2 teaspoon ground cumin
- 1/2 teaspoon ground coriander
- 1/4 teaspoon ground cinnamon
- Salt and pepper to taste
- 1 tablespoon olive oil
- Fresh cilantro for garnish (optional)

Instructions:

1. In a large pot, heat olive oil over medium heat.

2. Add diced onion and minced garlic to the pot. Cook for 2-3 minutes until softened and fragrant.

3. Pour in the vegetable broth and bring it to a simmer.

4. Add canned chickpeas, diced tomatoes, diced carrots, diced zucchini, ground cumin, ground coriander, and ground cinnamon to the pot. Cook for 25-30 minutes, until vegetables are tender.

5. Season with salt and pepper to taste.

6. Serve hot, garnished with fresh cilantro if desired.

SALADS RECIPES

Grilled Chicken and Avocado Salad

Serving for 1   Prep Time: 15 minutes

___

Calories: 350 kcal   Carbohydrates: 15 grams   Fiber: 7 grams   Protein: 30 grams

Healthy Fat: 20 grams

Ingredients:

- 4 oz. grilled chicken breast, sliced
- 1 cup mixed salad greens (spinach, arugula, lettuce)
- 1/4 avocado, sliced
- 1/4 cup cherry tomatoes, halved
- 1/4 cup cucumber, sliced
- 1 tablespoon olive oil
- 1 tablespoon balsamic vinegar
- Salt and pepper to taste
- Fresh basil leaves for garnish (optional)

Instructions:

1. In a large bowl, combine the mixed salad greens, sliced avocado, cherry tomatoes, and cucumber.
2. Add the grilled chicken breast slices on top of the salad.
3. In a small bowl, whisk together olive oil, balsamic vinegar, salt, and pepper to make the dressing.
4. Drizzle the dressing over the salad.
5. Toss gently to coat all ingredients evenly.
6. Garnish with fresh basil leaves if desired.
7. Serve immediately and enjoy this refreshing and nutritious grilled chicken and avocado salad.

Quinoa and Chickpea Salad

Serving for 1   Prep Time: 20 minutes

Calories: 320 kcal   Carbohydrates: 45 grams   Fiber: 10 grams   Protein: 12 grams

Healthy Fat: 10 grams

Ingredients:

- 1/2 cup cooked quinoa, cooled
- 1/4 cup canned chickpeas, drained and rinsed
- 1/4 cup diced cucumber
- 1/4 cup diced bell pepper (any color)
- 2 tablespoons chopped fresh parsley
- 1 tablespoon lemon juice
- 1 tablespoon olive oil
- 1/4 teaspoon ground cumin
- Salt and pepper to taste
- Lemon wedges for serving (optional)

Instructions:

1. In a large bowl, combine cooked quinoa, chickpeas, diced cucumber, diced bell pepper, and chopped fresh parsley.
2. In a small bowl, whisk together lemon juice, olive oil, ground cumin, salt, and pepper to make the dressing.
3. Drizzle the dressing over the quinoa salad.
4. Toss gently to coat all ingredients evenly.
5. Serve the salad in a bowl.
6. Garnish with lemon wedges if desired.
7. Serve immediately or refrigerate for later use.
8. Enjoy this flavorful and nutrient-rich quinoa and chickpea salad as a healthy meal option.

Salmon and Spinach Salad with Lemon-Dijon Dressing

Serving for 1   Prep Time: 20 minutes

Calories: 380 kcal   Carbohydrates: 10 grams   Fiber: 4 grams   Protein: 30 grams

Healthy Fat: 25 grams

Ingredients:

- 4 oz. grilled or baked salmon fillet
- 2 cups fresh spinach leaves
- 1/4 cup cherry tomatoes, halved
- 1/4 cup sliced cucumber
- 1/4 avocado, sliced
- 1 tablespoon olive oil
- 1 tablespoon fresh lemon juice
- 1 teaspoon Dijon mustard
- Salt and pepper to taste
- Fresh dill for garnish (optional)

Instructions:

1. In a large bowl, combine fresh spinach leaves, cherry tomatoes, sliced cucumber, and sliced avocado.
2. Place the grilled or baked salmon fillet on top of the salad.
3. In a small bowl, whisk together olive oil, fresh lemon juice, Dijon mustard, salt, and pepper to make the dressing.
4. Drizzle the dressing over the salad.
5. Toss gently to coat all ingredients evenly.
6. Garnish with fresh dill if desired.
7. Serve immediately and enjoy this nutritious and flavorful salmon and spinach salad.

Mediterranean Chickpea Salad

Serving for 1   Prep Time: 15 minutes

Calories: 330 kcal   Carbohydrates: 45 grams   Fiber: 12 grams   Protein: 15 grams

Healthy Fat: 10 grams

Ingredients:

- 1/2 cup canned chickpeas, drained and rinsed
- 1/4 cup diced cucumber
- 1/4 cup diced bell pepper (any color)
- 1/4 cup halved cherry tomatoes
- 2 tablespoons diced red onion
- 2 tablespoons chopped fresh parsley
- 1 tablespoon olive oil
- 1 tablespoon red wine vinegar
- 1/2 teaspoon dried oregano
- Salt and pepper to taste
- Crumbled feta cheese for garnish (optional)

Instructions:

1. In a large bowl, combine chickpeas, diced cucumber, diced bell pepper, halved cherry tomatoes, diced red onion, and chopped fresh parsley.
2. In a small bowl, whisk together olive oil, red wine vinegar, dried oregano, salt, and pepper to make the dressing.
3. Drizzle the dressing over the chickpea salad.
4. Toss gently to coat all ingredients evenly.
5. Garnish with crumbled feta cheese if desired.
6. Serve immediately or refrigerate for later use.
7. Enjoy this Mediterranean-inspired chickpea salad as a delicious and nutritious meal option.

Greek Quinoa Salad

Serving for 1   Prep Time: 15 minutes

Calories: 320 kcal   Carbohydrates: 45 grams   Fiber: 10 grams   Protein: 12 grams

Healthy Fat: 12 grams

Ingredients:

- 1/2 cup cooked quinoa, cooled
- 1/4 cup diced cucumber
- 1/4 cup halved cherry tomatoes
- 2 tablespoons diced red onion
- 2 tablespoons sliced Kalamata olives
- 2 tablespoons crumbled feta cheese
- 1 tablespoon chopped fresh parsley
- 1 tablespoon olive oil
- 1 tablespoon red wine vinegar
- 1/2 teaspoon dried oregano
- Salt and pepper to taste
- Lemon wedges for serving (optional)

Instructions:

1. In a large bowl, combine cooked quinoa, diced cucumber, halved cherry tomatoes, diced red onion, sliced Kalamata olives, crumbled feta cheese, and chopped fresh parsley.

2. In a small bowl, whisk together olive oil, red wine vinegar, dried oregano, salt, and pepper to make the dressing.

3. Drizzle the dressing over the quinoa salad.

4. Toss gently to coat all ingredients evenly.

5. Serve the salad in a bowl.

6. Garnish with lemon wedges if desired.

7. Serve immediately or refrigerate for later use.

8. Enjoy this Greek-inspired quinoa salad as a refreshing and nutritious meal option.

Spinach and Strawberry Salad with Balsamic Vinaigrette

Serving for 1   Prep Time: 10 minutes

Calories: 250 kcal   Carbohydrates: 30 grams   Fiber: 7 grams   Protein: 5 grams

Healthy Fat: 15 grams

Ingredients:

- 2 cups fresh spinach leaves
- 1/2 cup sliced strawberries
- 1/4 cup sliced almonds
- 1 tablespoon crumbled feta cheese
- 1 tablespoon olive oil
- 1 tablespoon balsamic vinegar
- 1/2 teaspoon honey
- Salt and pepper to taste

Instructions:

1. In a large bowl, combine fresh spinach leaves, sliced strawberries, sliced almonds, and crumbled feta cheese.

2. In a small bowl, whisk together olive oil, balsamic vinegar, honey, salt, and pepper to make the dressing.

3. Drizzle the dressing over the spinach and strawberry salad.

4. Toss gently to coat all ingredients evenly.

5. Serve immediately and enjoy this delightful spinach and strawberry salad with balsamic vinaigrette.

Tuna and White Bean Salad

Serving for 1   Prep Time: 10 minutes

Calories: 330 kcal   Carbohydrates: 30 grams   Fiber: 10 grams   Protein: 25 grams

Healthy Fat: 15 grams

Ingredients:

- 1/2 cup canned white beans, drained and rinsed
- 1/2 can (about 3 oz.) tuna, drained
- 1 cup mixed salad greens (spinach, arugula, lettuce)
- 1/4 cup cherry tomatoes, halved
- 1/4 cup sliced cucumber
- 1 tablespoon chopped red onion
- 1 tablespoon chopped fresh parsley
- 1 tablespoon olive oil
- 1 tablespoon red wine vinegar
- Salt and pepper to taste
- Lemon wedges for serving (optional)

Instructions:

1. In a large bowl, combine white beans, tuna, mixed salad greens, cherry tomatoes, sliced cucumber, chopped red onion, and chopped fresh parsley.
2. In a small bowl, whisk together olive oil, red wine vinegar, salt, and pepper to make the dressing.
3. Drizzle the dressing over the tuna and white bean salad.
4. Toss gently to coat all ingredients evenly.
5. Serve the salad in a bowl.
6. Garnish with lemon wedges if desired.
7. Serve immediately and enjoy this protein-rich and satisfying tuna and white bean salad.

Asian Chicken Salad

Serving for 1   Prep Time: 15 minutes

Calories: 300 kcal   Carbohydrates: 20 grams   Fiber: 5 grams   Protein: 25 grams

Healthy Fat: 15 grams

Ingredients:

- 4 oz. grilled chicken breast, sliced
- 2 cups shredded Napa cabbage
- 1/4 cup shredded carrots
- 1/4 cup diced red bell pepper
- 1/4 cup sliced cucumber
- 2 tablespoons chopped green onions
- 1 tablespoon chopped cilantro
- 1 tablespoon sesame seeds
- 1 tablespoon olive oil
- 1 tablespoon low-sodium soy sauce
- 1 tablespoon rice vinegar
- 1 teaspoon honey
- 1/2 teaspoon grated ginger
- Salt and pepper to taste

Instructions:

1. In a large bowl, combine shredded Napa cabbage, shredded carrots, diced red bell pepper, sliced cucumber, chopped green onions, and chopped cilantro.

2. Top the salad with sliced grilled chicken breast.

3. In a small bowl, whisk together olive oil, low-sodium soy sauce, rice vinegar, honey, grated ginger, salt, and pepper to make the dressing.

4. Drizzle the dressing over the Asian chicken salad.

5. Toss gently to coat all ingredients evenly.

6. Sprinkle sesame seeds over the salad.

7. Serve immediately and enjoy this flavorful and nutritious Asian chicken salad.

VEGETARIAN AND VEGAN CHOICES

Quinoa and Black Bean Stuffed Bell Peppers (Vegan)

Serving for 1   Prep Time: 20 minutes   Cook Time: 30 minutes

---

Calories: 350 kcal   Carbohydrates: 60 grams   Fiber: 15 grams   Protein: 15 grams

Healthy Fat: 5 grams

Ingredients:

- 1 bell pepper (any color), halved and seeds removed
- 1/2 cup cooked quinoa
- 1/4 cup canned black beans, drained and rinsed
- 1/4 cup diced tomatoes
- 1/4 cup diced onion
- 1/4 cup diced zucchini
- 1/4 teaspoon ground cumin
- 1/4 teaspoon chili powder
- Salt and pepper to taste
- Fresh cilantro for garnish (optional)

Instructions:

1. Preheat the oven to 375°F (190°C).
2. In a bowl, mix together cooked quinoa, black beans, diced tomatoes, diced onion, diced zucchini, ground cumin, chili powder, salt, and pepper.
3. Stuff each bell pepper half with the quinoa and black bean mixture.
4. Place the stuffed bell peppers in a baking dish.
5. Cover the baking dish with aluminum foil and bake in the preheated oven for 25-30 minutes, or until the bell peppers are tender.
6. Remove the foil and bake for an additional 5 minutes.
7. Garnish with fresh cilantro if desired.

Chickpea and Vegetable Stir-Fry (Vegetarian)

Serving for 1   Prep Time: 15 minutes   Cook Time: 15 minutes

---

Calories: 320 kcal   Carbohydrates: 45 grams   Fiber: 12 grams   Protein: 15 grams

Healthy Fat: 10 grams

Ingredients:

- 1/2 cup cooked chickpeas (canned or homemade)
- 1/2 cup mixed vegetables (such as bell peppers, broccoli, carrots)
- 1/4 cup diced onion
- 1 clove garlic, minced
- 1 tablespoon olive oil
- 1 tablespoon low-sodium soy sauce
- 1 tablespoon rice vinegar
- 1/2 teaspoon grated ginger
- 1/2 teaspoon sesame oil
- 1/4 teaspoon red pepper flakes (optional)
- Cooked brown rice for serving

Instructions:

1. Heat olive oil in a large skillet or wok over medium heat.

2. Add diced onion and minced garlic to the skillet. Cook for 2-3 minutes until softened and fragrant.

3. Add mixed vegetables to the skillet. Stir-fry for 5-7 minutes until vegetables are tender-crisp.

4. Add cooked chickpeas to the skillet. Stir to combine with the vegetables.

5. In a small bowl, whisk together low-sodium soy sauce, rice vinegar, grated ginger, sesame oil, and red pepper flakes (if using).

6. Pour the sauce over the chickpea and vegetable mixture in the skillet. Stir well to coat all ingredients evenly.

7. Cook for another 2-3 minutes, until the sauce has thickened slightly.

8. Serve the chickpea and vegetable stir-fry over cooked brown rice.

9. Enjoy this flavorful and satisfying vegetarian stir-fry as a nutritious meal option.

Lentil and Vegetable Curry (Vegan)

Serving for 1   Prep Time: 15 minutes   Cook Time: 30 minutes

Calories: 350 kcal   Carbohydrates: 55 grams   Fiber: 15 grams   Protein: 18 grams

Healthy Fat: 8 grams

Ingredients:

- 1/2 cup dry lentils, rinsed
- 1 cup diced tomatoes
- 1/2 cup diced onion
- 1/2 cup diced bell pepper (any color)
- 1/2 cup diced zucchini
- 1 clove garlic, minced

- 1 tablespoon olive oil
- 1 tablespoon curry powder
- 1/2 teaspoon ground turmeric
- 1/2 teaspoon ground cumin
- 1/4 teaspoon red pepper flakes (optional)
- Salt and pepper to taste
- Fresh cilantro for garnish (optional)

Instructions:

1. In a large pot, heat olive oil over medium heat.

2. Add diced onion and minced garlic to the pot. Cook for 2-3 minutes until softened and fragrant.

3. Stir in diced tomatoes, diced bell pepper, diced zucchini, curry powder, ground turmeric, ground cumin, red pepper flakes (if using), salt, and pepper.

4. Add rinsed lentils to the pot and stir to combine with the vegetables and spices.

5. Pour in enough water to cover the lentils and vegetables.

6. Bring the mixture to a boil, then reduce the heat to low and let it simmer for 25-30 minutes, or until the lentils are tender and the curry has thickened.

7. Taste and adjust seasoning if needed.

8. Serve hot, garnished with fresh cilantro if desired.

9. Enjoy this hearty and flavorful lentil and vegetable curry as a satisfying meal option.

Roasted Vegetable Quinoa Bowl (Vegetarian)

Serving for 1   Prep Time: 20 minutes   Cook Time: 25 minutes

Calories: 380 kcal   Carbohydrates: 55 grams   Fiber: 10 grams   Protein: 15 grams

Healthy Fat: 12 grams

Ingredients:

- 1/2 cup cooked quinoa
- 1/2 cup diced sweet potato
- 1/2 cup diced bell pepper (any color)
- 1/2 cup diced zucchini
- 1/4 cup diced red onion
- 1 tablespoon olive oil
- 1/2 teaspoon smoked paprika
- 1/2 teaspoon dried thyme
- Salt and pepper to taste
- 1 tablespoon balsamic vinegar

- 1 tablespoon chopped fresh parsley for garnish (optional)

Instructions:

1. Preheat the oven to 400°F (200°C).
2. In a bowl, toss diced sweet potato, diced bell pepper, diced zucchini, and diced red onion with olive oil, smoked paprika, dried thyme, salt, and pepper.
3. Spread the seasoned vegetables in a single layer on a baking sheet lined with parchment paper.
4. Roast the vegetables in the preheated oven for 20-25 minutes, or until they are tender and lightly browned, stirring halfway through.
5. In a serving bowl, layer cooked quinoa and roasted vegetables.
6. Drizzle balsamic vinegar over the quinoa and roasted vegetables.
7. Garnish with chopped fresh parsley if desired.
8. Serve warm and enjoy this delicious and nutritious roasted vegetable quinoa bowl.

Tofu and Vegetable Stir-Fry (Vegan)

Serving for 1   Prep Time: 15 minutes   Cook Time: 15 minutes

Calories: 320 kcal   Carbohydrates: 30 grams   Fiber: 10 grams   Protein: 15 grams

Healthy Fat: 15 grams

Ingredients:

- 4 oz. firm tofu, cubed
- 1 cup mixed vegetables (such as broccoli, bell peppers, snap peas)
- 1/4 cup sliced mushrooms
- 1/4 cup diced onion
- 1 clove garlic, minced
- 1 tablespoon low-sodium soy sauce
- 1 tablespoon rice vinegar

- 1 teaspoon sesame oil
- 1/2 teaspoon grated ginger
- 1/2 teaspoon cornstarch mixed with 1 tablespoon water
- 1 tablespoon olive oil
- Cooked brown rice for serving

Instructions:

1. In a large skillet or wok, heat olive oil over medium-high heat.
2. Add cubed tofu to the skillet and cook until golden brown on all sides, about 5-7 minutes. Remove tofu from the skillet and set aside.
3. In the same skillet, add sliced mushrooms, mixed vegetables, diced onion, and minced garlic. Stir-fry for 5-7 minutes until vegetables are tender-crisp.
4. In a small bowl, whisk together low-sodium soy sauce, rice vinegar, sesame oil, grated ginger, and cornstarch mixture.
5. Return the tofu to the skillet and pour the sauce over the tofu and vegetables.
6. Cook for another 2-3 minutes, stirring constantly, until the sauce has thickened.
7. Serve the tofu and vegetable stir-fry over cooked brown rice.
8. Enjoy this flavorful and protein-rich vegan stir-fry as a satisfying meal option.

Eggplant and Chickpea Tagine (Vegetarian)

Serving for 1   Prep Time: 20 minutes   Cook Time: 35 minutes

Calories: 300 kcal   Carbohydrates: 45 grams   Fiber: 12 grams   Protein: 10 grams
Healthy Fat: 8 grams

Ingredients:

- 1/2 cup canned chickpeas, drained and rinsed
- 1/2 eggplant, diced
- 1/2 cup diced tomatoes
- 1/4 cup diced onion
- 1/4 cup sliced carrots
- 1/4 cup sliced zucchini
- 1 clove garlic, minced
- 1 tablespoon olive oil

- 1 teaspoon ground cumin
- 1/2 teaspoon ground cinnamon
- 1/4 teaspoon ground coriander
- 1/4 teaspoon smoked paprika
- Salt and pepper to taste
- Chopped fresh cilantro for garnish (optional)

Instructions:

1. In a large skillet, heat olive oil over medium heat.

2. Add diced onion and minced garlic to the skillet. Cook for 2-3 minutes until softened and fragrant.

3. Stir in diced eggplant, diced tomatoes, sliced carrots, sliced zucchini, ground cumin, ground cinnamon, ground coriander, smoked paprika, salt, and pepper.

4. Add canned chickpeas to the skillet and stir to combine with the vegetables and spices.

5. Pour in enough water to cover the vegetables and chickpeas.

6. Bring the mixture to a boil, then reduce the heat to low and let it simmer for 25-30 minutes, or until the vegetables are tender and the sauce has thickened.

7. Taste and adjust seasoning if needed.

8. Serve hot, garnished with chopped fresh cilantro if desired.

9. Enjoy this aromatic and hearty eggplant and chickpea tagine as a delicious meal option.

Mediterranean Quinoa Salad (Vegetarian)

Serving for 1   Prep Time: 15 minutes

Calories: 320 kcal   Carbohydrates: 45 grams   Fiber: 10 grams   Protein: 10 grams

Healthy Fat: 12 grams

Ingredients:

- 1/2 cup cooked quinoa, cooled
- 1/4 cup diced cucumber
- 1/4 cup halved cherry tomatoes
- 2 tablespoons diced red onion
- 2 tablespoons sliced Kalamata olives
- 2 tablespoons crumbled feta cheese
- 1 tablespoon chopped fresh parsley
- 1 tablespoon olive oil
- 1 tablespoon red wine vinegar
- Salt and pepper to taste
- Lemon wedges for serving (optional)

Instructions:

1. In a large bowl, combine cooked quinoa, diced cucumber, halved cherry tomatoes, diced red onion, sliced Kalamata olives, crumbled feta cheese, and chopped fresh parsley.

2. In a small bowl, whisk together olive oil, red wine vinegar, salt, and pepper to make the dressing.

3. Drizzle the dressing over the quinoa salad.

4. Toss gently to coat all ingredients evenly.

5. Serve the salad in a bowl.

6. Garnish with lemon wedges if desired.

7. Serve immediately or refrigerate for later use.

Tofu and Vegetable Curry (Vegan)

Serving for 1   Prep Time: 15 minutes   Cook Time: 30 minutes

---

Calories: 350 kcal   Carbohydrates: 45 grams   Fiber: 15 grams   Protein: 18 grams

Healthy Fat: 8 grams

Ingredients:

- 1/2 cup dry lentils, rinsed
- 1 cup diced tomatoes
- 1/2 cup diced onion
- 1/2 cup diced bell pepper (any color)
- 1/2 cup diced zucchini
- 1 clove garlic, minced
- 1 tablespoon olive oil
- 1 tablespoon curry powder
- 1/2 teaspoon ground turmeric
- 1/2 teaspoon ground cumin
- 1/4 teaspoon red pepper flakes (optional)
- Salt and pepper to taste
- Fresh cilantro for garnish (optional)

Instructions:

1. In a large pot, heat olive oil over medium heat.
2. Add diced onion and minced garlic to the pot. Cook for 2-3 minutes until softened and fragrant.
3. Stir in diced tomatoes, diced bell pepper, diced zucchini, curry powder, ground turmeric, ground cumin, red pepper flakes (if using), salt, and pepper.
4. Add rinsed lentils to the pot and stir to combine with the vegetables and spices.
5. Pour in enough water to cover the lentils and vegetables.
6. Bring the mixture to a boil, then reduce the heat to low and let it simmer for 25-30 minutes, or until the lentils are tender and the curry has thickened.
7. Taste and adjust seasoning if needed.
8. Serve hot, garnished with fresh cilantro if desired..

KIDNEY-SAFE SNACK IDEAS

Avocado and Cottage Cheese Rice Cakes

Serving for 1   Prep Time: 5 minutes

Calories: 200 kcal   Carbohydrates: 15 grams   Fiber: 4 grams   Protein: 10 grams

Healthy Fat: 12 grams

Ingredients:

- 2 rice cakes (choose low-sodium if available)
- 1/4 ripe avocado, mashed
- 2 tablespoons low-fat cottage cheese
- Salt and pepper to taste
- Optional toppings: sliced cucumber, cherry tomatoes, or a sprinkle of sesame seeds

Instructions:

1. Spread mashed avocado evenly onto the rice cakes.
2. Top each rice cake with a tablespoon of low-fat cottage cheese.
3. Season with salt and pepper to taste.
4. If desired, add sliced cucumber, cherry tomatoes, or a sprinkle of sesame seeds on top for extra flavor and texture.
5. Serve immediately and enjoy this kidney-safe and diabetes-friendly snack!

Almond Butter and Apple Slices

Serving for 1   Prep Time: 5 minutes

Calories: 180 kcal   Carbohydrates: 15 grams   Fiber: 3 grams   Protein: 5 grams

Healthy Fat: 10 grams

Ingredients:

- 1 medium apple, sliced
- 1 tablespoon almond butter (choose unsweetened and no-salt-added varieties)

Instructions:

1. Wash and slice the apple into thin slices.
2. Spread almond butter on each apple slice.
3. Arrange the apple slices on a plate or serve them in a bowl.
4. If desired, sprinkle cinnamon on top for added flavor.
5. Serve immediately and enjoy this kidney-safe and diabetes-friendly snack!

Greek Yogurt Parfait with Berries

Serving for 1   Prep Time: 5 minutes

Calories: 180 kcal   Carbohydrates: 20 grams   Fiber: 4 grams   Protein: 15 grams
Healthy Fat: 6 grams

Ingredients:

- 1/2 cup plain Greek yogurt (choose low-fat or non-fat)
- 1/4 cup mixed berries (such as strawberries, blueberries, raspberries)
- 1 tablespoon chopped nuts (such as almonds, walnuts)
- 1 teaspoon honey or maple syrup (optional)

Instructions:

1. In a small bowl or glass, layer plain Greek yogurt with mixed berries.
2. Sprinkle chopped nuts on top of the yogurt and berries.
3. If desired, drizzle honey or maple syrup over the parfait for added sweetness.
4. Serve immediately and enjoy this kidney-safe and diabetes-friendly snack!

Cucumber Hummus Bites

Serving for 1   Prep Time: 10 minutes

Calories: 150 kcal   Carbohydrates: 15 grams   Fiber: 4 grams   Protein: 5 grams

Healthy Fat: 8 grams

Ingredients:

- 1 small cucumber, sliced into rounds
- 2 tablespoons hummus (choose low-sodium if available)
- 1 tablespoon chopped fresh parsley or cilantro
- Optional toppings: sliced cherry tomatoes, olives, or a sprinkle of paprika

Instructions:

1. Arrange cucumber slices on a plate.
2. Place a small dollop of hummus on each cucumber slice.
3. Sprinkle chopped fresh parsley or cilantro on top of the hummus.
4. If desired, add sliced cherry tomatoes, olives, or a sprinkle of paprika for extra flavor.
5. Serve immediately and enjoy this kidney-safe and diabetes-friendly snack!

Veggie Sticks with Yogurt Dip

Serving for 1   Prep Time: 10 minutes

Calories: 120 kcal   Carbohydrates: 15 grams   Fiber: 4 grams   Protein: 8 grams

Healthy Fat: 4 grams

Ingredients:

- 1 small carrot, cut into sticks
- 1 small cucumber, cut into sticks
- 1 stalk celery, cut into sticks
- 1/4 cup plain Greek yogurt (choose low-fat or non-fat)
- 1/2 teaspoon lemon juice
- 1/4 teaspoon garlic powder
- Salt and pepper to taste
- Fresh parsley for garnish (optional)

Instructions:

1. Arrange carrot sticks, cucumber sticks, and celery sticks on a plate.

2. In a small bowl, mix together plain Greek yogurt, lemon juice, garlic powder, salt, and pepper to make the dip.

3. Transfer the yogurt dip to a small serving bowl and place it alongside the veggie sticks.

4. Garnish with fresh parsley if desired.

5. Serve immediately and enjoy this kidney-safe and diabetes-friendly snack!

Almond and Date Energy Bites

Serving for 1   Prep Time: 15 minutes

Calories: 150 kcal   Carbohydrates: 15 grams   Fiber: 3 grams   Protein: 5 grams

Healthy Fat: 8 grams

Ingredients:

- 1/4 cup almonds
- 3 pitted dates
- 1 tablespoon unsweetened shredded coconut
- 1 tablespoon almond butter (choose unsweetened and no-salt-added varieties)
- 1/2 teaspoon cinnamon
- Optional toppings: cocoa powder, chopped nuts, or shredded coconut for rolling

Instructions:

1. In a food processor, combine almonds, pitted dates, shredded coconut, almond butter, and cinnamon.
2. Pulse until the mixture forms a dough-like consistency.
3. Roll the mixture into small balls using your hands.
4. If desired, roll the energy bites in cocoa powder, chopped nuts, or shredded coconut for extra flavor and texture.
5. Place the energy bites on a plate or baking sheet lined with parchment paper.
6. Refrigerate for at least 30 minutes to firm up.
7. Serve chilled and enjoy these kidney-safe and diabetes-friendly energy bites as a nutritious snack!

SUGAR-FREE DESSERTS

Sugar-Free Chia Seed Pudding

Serving for 1   Prep Time: 5 minutes   Chilling Time: 4 hours or overnight

---

Calories: 200 kcal   Carbohydrates: 15 grams   Fiber: 10 grams   Protein: 5 grams

Healthy Fat: 12 grams

Ingredients:

- 2 tablespoons chia seeds
- 1/2 cup unsweetened almond milk (or any milk of your choice)
- 1/4 teaspoon vanilla extract
- Stevia or erythritol to taste (optional)
- Fresh berries or sliced fruits for topping (optional)

Instructions:

1. In a small bowl or jar, combine chia seeds, unsweetened almond milk, vanilla extract, and stevia or erythritol if desired.
2. Stir well to ensure the chia seeds are evenly distributed.
3. Cover the bowl or jar and refrigerate for at least 4 hours or overnight, allowing the chia seeds to absorb the liquid and thicken.
4. Once the pudding has set, give it a good stir.
5. Serve chilled and top with fresh berries or sliced fruits if desired.
6. Enjoy this sugar-free chia seed pudding as a guilt-free dessert option!

Sugar-Free Baked Apples

Serving for 1   Prep Time: 10 minutes   Baking Time: 25 minutes

---

Calories: 150 kcal   Carbohydrates: 30 grams   Fiber: 5 grams   Protein: 2 grams

Healthy Fat: 3 grams

Ingredients:

- 1 medium apple, cored and halved
- 1 tablespoon unsweetened applesauce
- 1/2 teaspoon ground cinnamon
- 1/4 teaspoon ground nutmeg
- 1/4 teaspoon vanilla extract
- Stevia or erythritol to taste (optional)
- Chopped nuts or seeds for topping (optional)
- Greek yogurt or whipped cream for serving (optional)

Instructions:

1. Preheat the oven to 350°F (175°C).
2. In a small bowl, mix together unsweetened applesauce, ground cinnamon, ground nutmeg, vanilla extract, and stevia or erythritol if desired.
3. Place the apple halves in a baking dish, cut side up.
4. Spoon the applesauce mixture evenly over the apple halves.
5. Cover the baking dish with aluminum foil and bake in the preheated oven for 20 minutes.
6. Remove the foil and bake for an additional 5 minutes, or until the apples are tender.
7. Serve the sugar-free baked apples warm, topped with chopped nuts or seeds if desired.
8. Optionally, serve with a dollop of Greek yogurt or whipped cream for extra indulgence.

Sugar-Free Peanut Butter Chocolate Chia Pudding

Serving for 1   Prep Time: 5 minutes   Chilling Time: 4 hours or overnight

---

Calories: 250 kcal   Carbohydrates: 15 grams   Fiber: 10 grams   Protein: 8 grams

Healthy Fat: 18 grams

Ingredients:

- 2 tablespoons chia seeds
- 1/2 cup unsweetened almond milk (or any milk of your choice)
- 1 tablespoon unsweetened cocoa powder
- 1 tablespoon sugar-free peanut butter
- Stevia or erythritol to taste (optional)
- Chopped peanuts or dark chocolate shavings for topping (optional)

Instructions:

1. In a small bowl or jar, combine chia seeds, unsweetened almond milk, cocoa powder, sugar-free peanut butter, and stevia or erythritol if desired.
2. Stir well to ensure the ingredients are evenly mixed.
3. Cover the bowl or jar and refrigerate for at least 4 hours or overnight, allowing the chia seeds to absorb the liquid and thicken.
4. Once the pudding has set, give it a good stir.
5. Serve chilled and top with chopped peanuts or dark chocolate shavings if desired.
6. Enjoy this indulgent sugar-free peanut butter chocolate chia pudding as a guilt-free dessert option!

Sugar-Free Coconut Mango Popsicles

Serving for 1   Prep Time: 10 minutes   Freezing Time: 4-6 hours

---

Calories: 120 kcal   Carbohydrates: 20 grams   Fiber: 4 grams   Protein: 1 gram

Healthy Fat: 4 grams

Ingredients:

- 1/2 cup chopped ripe mango
- 1/4 cup unsweetened coconut milk
- 1 tablespoon unsweetened shredded coconut
- Stevia or erythritol to taste (optional)

Instructions:

1. In a blender, combine chopped ripe mango, unsweetened coconut milk, and stevia or erythritol if desired.
2. Blend until smooth and well combined.
3. Stir in unsweetened shredded coconut.
4. Pour the mixture into popsicle molds.
5. Insert popsicle sticks into the molds.
6. Freeze for 4-6 hours, or until the popsicles are completely frozen.
7. Once frozen, remove the popsicles from the molds and serve immediately.
8. Enjoy these refreshing and tropical sugar-free coconut mango popsicles as a delightful dessert or snack!

Sugar-Free Berry Yogurt Parfait

Serving for 1   Prep Time: 5 minutes

Calories: 180 kcal   Carbohydrates: 20 grams   Fiber: 5 grams   Protein: 10 grams

Healthy Fat: 6 grams

Ingredients:

- 1/2 cup plain Greek yogurt (choose low-fat or non-fat)
- 1/4 cup mixed berries (such as strawberries, blueberries, raspberries)
- 1 tablespoon chopped nuts (such as almonds, walnuts)
- 1 teaspoon sugar-free sweetener (stevia or erythritol), optional

Instructions:

1. In a small bowl or glass, layer plain Greek yogurt with mixed berries.
2. Sprinkle chopped nuts on top of the yogurt and berries.
3. Optionally, add a teaspoon of sugar-free sweetener for extra sweetness, if desired.
4. Serve immediately and enjoy this sugar-free berry yogurt parfait as a guilt-free dessert or snack!

Sugar-Free Baked Pears with Cinnamon

Serving for 1   Prep Time: 10 minutes   Baking Time: 25 minutes

---

Calories: 120 kcal Carbohydrates: 30 grams   Fiber: 5 grams   Protein: 1 gram

Healthy Fat: 0 grams

Ingredients:

- 1 medium pear, halved and cored
- 1/2 teaspoon ground cinnamon
- 1 teaspoon sugar-free sweetener (stevia or erythritol), optional
- Fresh lemon juice, for drizzling

Instructions:

1. Preheat the oven to 375°F (190°C).
2. Place the pear halves, cut side up, on a baking sheet lined with parchment paper.
3. Sprinkle ground cinnamon over the pear halves.
4. Optionally, add a teaspoon of sugar-free sweetener for extra sweetness, if desired.
5. Drizzle fresh lemon juice over the pears.
6. Bake in the preheated oven for 20-25 minutes, or until the pears are tender and slightly caramelized.
7. Remove from the oven and let cool slightly before serving.
8. Enjoy these warm and comforting sugar-free baked pears with cinnamon as a delicious and healthy dessert option!

I want to extend my deepest gratitude to you to have taken your time to explore "CKD Stage 3 and Diabetes Type 2 Cookbook." Your interest in this book means the world to me, and I am genuinely honored to have the opportunity to share this resource with you.

As an author, there is nothing more valuable than hearing feedback from readers like yourself. Your honest reviews not only provide invaluable insights into how this book has impacted your life but also help other potential readers make informed decisions about whether this book is the right fit for them.

I kindly request that if you have found value in "CKD Stage 3 and Diabetes Type 2 Cookbook," would you consider leaving a review on Amazon? Your thoughts and opinions matter greatly, and your review could make all the difference in helping others discover the benefits of this book.

Additionally, I invite you to follow me as an author on Amazon to stay updated on future releases, special promotions, and exclusive content. Your support means the world to me, and I am committed to continuing to provide valuable resources to support your journey toward optimal health and well-being.

Once again, thank you from the bottom of my heart for your support and for being a part of this community. Together, let's continue to inspire and empower one another on our paths to wellness.

Use your camera to scan this QR Code or visit amazon.com and search author name "Lori J. Garcia"

Made in the USA
Las Vegas, NV
10 December 2024

13821898R00059